NUTRITI

RUDOLF HAUSCHKA

Nutrition

TRANSLATED FROM THE GERMAN
BY MARJORIE SPOCK
AND MARY T RICHARDS

RUDOLF STEINER PRESS
LONDON

ERNÄHRUNGSLEHRE
© 1951 VITTORIO KLOSTERMANN
FRANKFURT AM MAIN

First Published in English by
Vincent Stuart and John M. Watkins Ltd 1967

Second Edition 1983, published by
Rudolf Steiner Press,
38 Museum Street, London WC1A 1LP

British Library Cataloguing in Publication Data

Hauschka, Rudolf
  Nutrition.
  1. Nutrition   2. Anthroposophy
  I. Title   II. Ernährungslehre. *English*
  641.1   TX353
  ISBN 0-85440-422-8

Printed and bound in Great Britain at
The Camelot Press Ltd, Southampton

Contents

CONTENTS

List of Illustrations

Foreword to the First English Edition (1966)

The 'New Approach to Nutrition' presented in the following pages should be considered as a contribution to the total subject of human nutrition. It is written from a standpoint almost wholly unprecedented in our time. The author feels that he should try to raise the whole subject to an entirely new plane, for in his view the fact that man is a being of soul and spirit, whose connection with the universe around him can be ascertained not only by natural-scientific research but by the methods of Spiritual Science as well, is a consideration of first importance in matters of nutrition.

It is not the author's intention either to write a cook book or to compile an encyclopedia of isolated facts on the physiology of nutrition or on food chemistry. This work is rather a first attempt at presenting a new view of the physiology of digestion and of the ponderable and imponderable qualities of foodstuffs. Today's urgent need prompts him to offer it in its present still rather sketchy form.

In very ancient times nutrition was a matter regulated by the spiritual leadership of a race or people. Later it was directed from mystical or cultural centres. Though such diets have long remained matters of religious precept, in recent times people have come to depend more on instinct as a guide to sensible eating habits. But modern man has lost even this, along with other instincts. It is therefore timely to make up for what he has lost by working through to a clear understanding of the facts.

Admirable and astonishing as is the wealth of facts brought to light by the orthodox nutritional science of the day, its sheer extent is so overwhelming as to make any spiritual thread of connection hard to find. The task is made no easier by the way this science insists on applying the prevailing technological approach to both biology and physiology. This only adds to the confusion that already surrounds problems in this field.

The author feels it is particularly important to treat problems of nutrition in an evolutionary perspective. The right questions cannot even be posed without achieving some preliminary

ix

clarity as to the stage of development modern man has reached. There can never be any such thing as a rule applicable to every period. But to see where man stands at a given moment in his evolution is to know what foods are suited to him.

Rudolf Steiner has provided the foundation for just such an approach in his Anthroposophy. The author frequently indicates the epistemological background which moved him to submit a work based on so entirely new a way of thinking.

The author's fourteen years of work at the Clinical-Therapeutic Institute at Arlesheim near Basel afforded him excellent training and led to many fruitful insights. It was in the Institute's laboratories, moreover, that the experiments described below were carried out. Working with the other doctors on the staff proved highly stimulating. Most special thanks are due to the late Dr I. Wegman, directrice of the Institute, who always felt a deep connection with and interest in the research work done there. Her co-workers still feel themselves fully obligated to pursue the spiritual goals she set.

I think too, with gratitude, of stimulating talks with friends, in particular those with Dr H. Walter of Ascona, Dr J. Schulz of Stuttgart, and Dr O. Eckstein, recently deceased, of Arlesheim. And my thanks are due to all my colleagues, especially Frl Gertrude Weinmar, one of those most responsible for the development of the Capillary-Dynamic method.

This volume was conceived as a sequel to my book, *The Nature of Substance*, published in German in 1942 and in English in 1966. The latter lays a thorough foundation for understanding 'A New Approach to Nutrition'. Many references will therefore be made to pertinent passages in the earlier book, though on the other hand certain portions will have to be repeated here. In the author's mind, however, the two books constitute a single work.

Dietary suggestions are deliberately avoided here, while on the other hand every effort has been made to impart facts leading to a real grasp of the subject. The reader must be left wholly free to draw such conclusions as his insight dictates. The author would consider his job poorly done if readers gathered the impression that by adopting a particular diet they could 'eat their way into heaven'. This would be most mistaken. Food is only a support in striving for a developmental goal, and can never be a substitute for spiritual effort.

The author hopes he will not mistakenly be thought to advocate the following of a set of nutritional practices under any and all conditions just because they are described as right in certain circumstances. Today people must – if necessary – be able to take everything in their stride, and those who persist through thick and thin in carrying out some diet they deem essential are certainly unpleasant company. Social considerations are not insignificant aspects of the healthful life.

In closing, let me express heartfelt thanks to my publisher for the kindly, helpful manner of his collaboration and last but not least the translators Marjorie Spock and Mary Richards for their endeavour to preserve the life and colour of the original manuscript.

RUDOLF HAUSCHKA, D.Sc.

Eckwälden, Christmas 1966

Foreword to the Second English Edition (1983)

Since this book was first published, over thirty years ago in Germany, and some twenty years ago in English translation, interest has grown significantly in scientific views like those of the late Dr Rudolf Hauschka, that directly challenge the assumptions of materialistic science. This volume is being reprinted, with minor corrections, with the purpose of stimulating this interest further.

It must be borne in mind, however, that since the time when the text was written, research in biological chemistry and physics, notably vitamins (see Chapter XV), has progressed enormously, and many basic questions have been resolved.

The main reason for delaying the reprinting of this volume derives from uncertainties about, and lack of independent corroboration of, the various experiments described. It has not proved possible to repeat them based simply on the all too brief and generalised descriptions given in the text, or so far to trace the original experimental documents.

While this may detract from the scientific merit of the book, it must be appreciated that, on the other hand, it has not been demonstrated conclusively that the experiments cannot be repeated in their original form. The subtle and delicate effects within the realm of the four ethers cannot be so readily demonstrated in laboratory experiments, as purely inorganic or electromagnetic forces can. The Science Group of the Anthroposophical Society in Great Britain is continuing to seek to clarify this vital issue.

Hence the Science Group considers that the reprinting of this volume meanwhile is justified subject to this written qualification, and that many of Dr Hauschka's imaginative insights and seminal ideas contained herein are in themselves a most valuable contribution to our scientific understanding of chemistry and the living world. The Group welcomes any written experimental evidence, either for or against the subject matter of this book, in particular published reports or articles. Correspondence should be addressed in the first place to the Secretary of the Group, Rudolf Steiner House, 35 Park Road, London NW1 6XT.

ROBERT KERSEY GREEN

June 1983

CHAPTER ONE

Man and the Kingdoms of Nature

Seeds are quickened in the earth's dark night,
Plants spring green in vibrant air and light,
Fruits are ripened by the strong sun's might.
So quickens the soul in the heart's warm deep,
So flourishes the spirit in the wide world's keep,
So ripen human powers for God to reap.

RUDOLF STEINER
(table grace, freely rendered by the translators)

In this natural-scientific age, nutrition is regarded as a series of processes whose course is determined by physico-chemical laws. Surveying the magnificent results of research and progress in chemical technology, chemical science feels itself particularly justified in regarding and studying nutritional processes exactly as it does a series of chemical reactions taking place in the laboratory. Modern physiological chemistry is dominated by the quantitative viewpoint. Today's nutritional physiology highlights the balanced diet, consisting of essential proteins, fats, carbohydrates and salts; and vitamins and other active ingredients are looked at in the same way. Vitamin C, for example, is identified with ascorbic acid, and indications are then given in milligram-percentages as to the ascorbic acid content of a food. This is typical of the modern viewpoint, which sees man as a mechanism, complex perhaps, but still in the category of objects that can be weighed, counted, measured, manipulated and repaired.

This way of investigating man and human nutrition is a necessary consequence of the prevailing view of the world and nature, which subscribes to the theory that the earth and the entire solar system have emerged from a primal nebula and now circle one another as material cosmic bodies held in position by the law of gravity. In this grey universe man is the highest animal, having – by struggle and selection – come out on top of a long line of living creatures spawned in this nebulous primal generation. Thus man stands in a mechanical universe, himself a mere mechanism, lacking any moral stamina or responsibility, caught up in an evolutionary course devoid of meaning.

I

This is quite a recent development. Not long ago mankind still lived so deeply in the truths of religion that the story of creation found in Genesis and many other legends had a reality so vivid as to make our modern scientific abstractions pale by contrast. In olden times man felt himself wholly one with the creative sources of all being, with the spiritual powers that upheld evolution.

This sense of resting in the lap of the gods had its earthly counterpart in man's feeling of belonging to groups such as family, tribe and nation, which continued right into the Middle Ages. He was equally bound to religious dogmas and traditions, so much so that it appears natural, in the light of a larger view of history, to ask whether the dawning of the scientific age did not indeed spell needed progress. Science certainly freed man from this sort of bondage and kindled in him the divine spark of freedom without which there could be no further step in the direction of genuine human love; for only deeds of love born of freedom deserve the name.

The dilemma in which man now finds himself is therefore twofold. On the one hand he is caught up in a materialistic view of world and nature totally devoid of spirit. On the other hand he already feels the ego-kernel of a free individuality springing up within him. This raises the question whether we will be able to penetrate again to the wholeness of creation through the scientific attitude of soul built up in the last three or four centuries. The methods of science attest to the selfless character of its seeking after knowledge. This is witnessed in the biographies of many of its greatest men, whose basic attitude was that of deep conscientiousness even in the midst of tragic consequences. The scientific conscience is indeed an eternal treasure stored up by mankind in the course of these centuries. It can flourish only in an atmosphere of freedom, where doubt and even despair have often accompanied those searchers on a path of knowledge limited to pure sense perception and causality. When scientific theories of today have long since become a laughing stock as outdated absurdities, the scientific conscience will still go on as an imperishable fruit of the scientific age, serving as a sustaining moral force in the future evolution of mankind.

This was fully confirmed by Rudolf Steiner, whose own

epistemological writings were based on Goethe. Goethe showed in his scientific works how a mode of thought grounded in reality rather than lost in abstractions leads to completely new insights into nature. Even though present day scientists are not inclined to recognize Goethe's great achievements, any unprejudiced student of his findings on colour and metamorphosis immediately glimpses a new dawn breaking on the scientific front. And just as Aristotle was the first to bring Plato's wonderful imaginative representations of cosmic fact into the form of logical concepts so was Rudolf Steiner the first to carry the Goethean concept beyond the point where Goethe left it by showing how reality is grasped in thinking.

In his book, *The Nature of Substance*, the author kept this background of spiritual history in mind in his descriptions of the behaviour of substances. The mineral and plant kingdoms occupied the centre of the stage in these descriptions. Other investigators, e.g., Poppelbaum in his *Man and Animal*, have explored the question: is man really the highest animal, or should we take an entirely different view in order to reach a factual answer?

A comparison of man with the higher animals leads to the surprising fact that from the bodily standpoint man can certainly not be called the crown of creation. The human body is indeed incomparably nobler, more versatile and well-balanced than the animal's. But the human hand, for example, is far less perfectly equipped for specific tasks than the lion's paw, the horse's hoof, the digging foot of the mole, the fins, wings and extremities of other creatures. The human hand is noble, but 'leaving out of account its infinite latent possibilities, then, considered purely as a tool formed for a particular task it is the most imperfect of all'.*
This point of view leads directly to the conclusion that the human hand achieves versatility and balance simply through the restraint with which it stops short of developing in any specialized direction.

One can sense too that the whole human form has stayed close to its archetype, while animal forms represent a falling away from it. This archetypal purity comes to noblest expression in the

---

* *Man and Animal*, Hermann Poppelbaum, Ph.D., Anthroposophical Publishing Co., London, Anthroposophic Press, Inc., New York, 1931.

3

human head. Animal heads have developed into tools (as in the case of birds, which use their beaks as limbs), while human heads preserve a cosmic roundness. 'The perfecting of the animal head as a tool for physical operation on its environment robs it of the universality that distinguishes the human head.' The restraint practised by man with respect to his bodily development, which keeps him from the animal's precipitate rush into a fixed, specialized form, gives him his unique capacity for spiritual activity.

That a continuing development does not necessarily mean higher development is demonstrated when we compare the head of a very young ape with that of the full-grown creature. The young ape's head is beautifully rounded. It is a shocking experience to study the change whereby the finely modelled round of the back of its head and its brow is transformed into the repulsively distorted adult cranium. 'And this unrecognizable distortion takes its course in 4-5 years, i.e., in a space of time in which the face of a little human child has scarcely altered. While the child's face retains for a long time something like its original form, in the ape there takes place such a loss of all human characteristics as well nigh moves us to pity.'

The fact that animals develop into fixed, specialised forms is shown most convincingly in the change that has had to be made in diagramming the tree of descent (Fig. 1).

A few decades ago, man was held to be descended from apes. Today's investigators ascribe both man and ape to a common, unknown ancestor. Mammals, once thought to be further developments of the reptilian, are now believed to derive from the same primal form. While in the earlier tree of descent names of groups, fossils or purely speculative ancestors stud the trunk at fork after fork, today nothing but a series of question marks is found there.

Thus it becomes ever clearer that the primal human form was creation's first handiwork, and that animals represent physically fixed deviations in the direction of some limited specialization. Man is nature's firstborn child, and he stays human just because he finds it possible to hold in check those impulses that lead to the modelling of the various animal forms. The following metaphor pictures this to perfection: a balloon floating over the ocean keeps losing elevation, and is finally threatened with submersion. What can its passenger do to avert catastrophe? He throws ballast overboard in order to stay in the air long enough to get safely to land. In the same way man, faced with the danger of premature hardening, threw the animal kingdom out of his being. Thus he rid

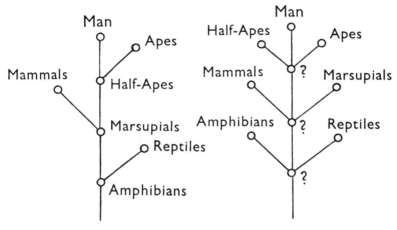

Fig. 1

Change in the tree of descent. Known forms are relegated to branch terminals while the forks on the trunk fill with question marks. (From Poppelbaum: *Man and Animal*.)

himself of a large part of his instincts, passions and desires, which then incarnated in the shapes of beasts. We owe to them our development into human beings.

When the early form of the ancestral tree is replaced by the following picture of human evolution, the question arises as to what kept man from sinking into a one-sided rigidity.

It was the spark of divinity present in us as the seed of our human development through the ages, known today as the free, individual ego. In *The Nature of Substance* I attempted to show creation to be a process whereby immaterial, spiritual being evolves into material, visible forms. It could be said in further exposition that the mineral and plant kingdoms may be regarded as evolutionary laggards like the animals, as cast-offs, as fixed

forms of earlier stages of human development. Man ever dominated the creative plan as an archetypal, spiritual form.

This becomes clearer the more we open ourselves to the thought
that man and earth with its animals, flowers, rocks are a single,
indivisible community; that nature's kingdoms are part of our
very being, genetically linked with us, belonging to us in mutual
dependence; that, morally speaking, we are responsible for them.
To feel a deep obligation to redeem them is not sentimental, for
they fell in order that we might rise to human stature.

No wonder poets and artists have so often expressed feelings of
this kind. Such a motif of redemption is found in the Good Friday

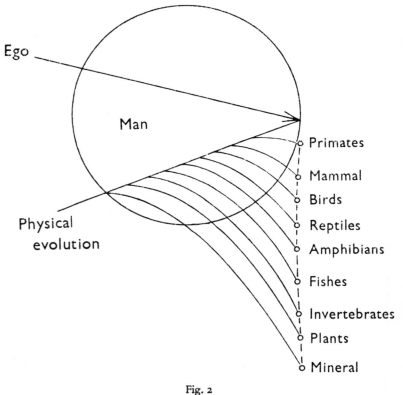

Fig. 2

Man as the archetype of creation. The psychical and spiritual aspects of becoming
human (Freely rendered from Poppelbaum: *Man and Animal.*)

Spell in Wagner's *Parsifal*: 'You weep – and lo! the meadows laugh.' The first redeeming step consists in learning to know the kingdoms of nature for what they are and according them their proper place in the great spiritual community of creation. The second step is taken when they are used as food. For what is nutrition but an inclusion of nature's kingdoms in our human-ness? When its mysteries are approached in the right mood we find them to be communion with the earth and its creatures.

THE WASHING OF FEET

I thank you, silent stones of earth,
In homage deep before you bending.
You helped the plant in me to birth.

I thank you, ground and green, in praise
And homage deep before you bending,
Whom you to creature-soul did raise.

I thank you, beast and plant and stone,
In homage deep before you bending.
Through you my human crown was won.

O man, our lowly thanks give we,
In homage deep before thee bending.
Because thou art, we too may be.

In thanks that bind the heavens around
–World linked to world in thanks unending –
The mighty choruses resound.

CHRISTIAN MORGENSTERN
(freely rendered by the translators)

CHAPTER TWO

Digestion

Man is connected with the surrounding world in three distinct ways: through his senses, his breathing and his nutriment. The following pages will show that the substances and forces entering and permeating his body in the above three ways interweave and become one single whole. These three processes take place on three different levels, with breathing in the middle. The life engendered by the senses is body-building of a more refined and spiritual kind, while the cruder material process usually meant by the term nutrition takes place at the opposite pole. Breathing is so essential to life as to be the obvious basis of the body-soul connection. It is a process not to any great extent under human control, but rather consonant with cosmic rhythms. In *The Nature of Substance* I showed that the rhythm of breathing, with its 18 breaths per minute and 25,920 breaths per day, is related to the 25,920 sun-years of a cosmic day. But if we did nothing but breathe we would always be asleep, and the world and our own bodily processes could enter our consciousness only in the form of dreams. It takes the waking state to call the two polar opposites of sense-perception and nutrition into action.

We transform the surrounding world into concepts by means of our senses. This is a way of saying that as our souls digest the world, a soul content is embodied in us. In a coarser kind of feeding on the world, we take in its substances and transform them in a physical digestion. Current nutritional physiology regards only the latter process as lying within its province. But man is a totality, and one thing conditions another. And indeed, none of the magnificent and exact findings in the narrower field of the metabolism in the least contradicts the broader view held by spiritual science.

Let us now consider the usual course of digestion.

As foods pass through the digestive system they are progressively broken down and dissolved. They are first mechanically ground and moistened with saliva in the mouth through the chewing action. Then chemical activity sets in as glands of the

8

mouth and throat are stimulated to secrete ptyalin and other substances. The pepsin secretions of the stomach are chiefly responsible for breaking proteins down into the form of peptones. Pancreatic secretions further reduce these to peptoids in the small intestine and there continue the work of dissolution already begun by saliva in the mouth on fats and carbohydrates. Other intestinal secretions finally break up every ingested substance into the smallest, finest building material imaginable: proteins into amino acids, by way of peptones and peptoids; carbohydrates into sugars; and fats into glycerine and fatty acids. The thoroughly dissolved chyme now passes by way of the resorptive villi right through the intestinal wall and into the true digestive zone.

What happens now?

It is only too easy to picture the process taking place on the far side of the intestinal wall as a gradual one of building human tissue up again, in its own way analogous to the dissolution that took place on the other side. The processes at work in the stomach and intestines are so clear and unmistakable in every least detail as to mislead the student into assuming that those occurring beyond the intestinal wall are similar in kind and just as clear. It happens all too frequently that knowledge gained in one field is simply transferred to others where it does not necessarily apply at all. An outstanding example is that of Newtonian physics. This system sufficed for dealing with conditions on or near the surface of the earth. But when it was projected into cosmic space, it soon proved inadequate or even downright erroneous, and the relativity theory had to be evolved to supply the necessary correction. Liebig's agricultural chemistry also errs, as was pointed out in *The Nature of Substance*, in assuming exclusively atomistic laws to obtain in plant growth, a field governed by the wholly different laws of metamorphosis.

The breakdown of foodstuff's that continues up to the point where they reach the intestinal wall is essentially identical with that occurring in laboratory reduction of protein, carbohydrates and fats when these are treated in retorts with appropriate reagents. It is even possible to model industrial procedures on certain phases of the digestive process occurring in the stomach and intestines, as, for example, in soap-making when fats are separated

9

by fermentation, in the process of changing starches into sucrose in brewery diastasis, or in the use of rennet ferment in making cheese. One is justified in thinking of the digestive tract from the mouth to the intestinal wall as part of a thoroughly familiar world known through ordinary means of research, a world in which physico-chemical laws are to some extent at least still valid.

But what of further developments on the other side of the wall?

Modern physiology's supposition, based on concepts current in chemistry, that a gradual synthesis takes place there does not quite apply. Otherwise we would rediscover in chyle and lymph the same building substances already found in the intestinal tract, for example the protein elements, amino acids, peptoids and peptones. But what we actually find in chyle and lymph is complete human protein! And such elements of broken down protein as appear in the bloodstream come, not from the intestines, but from muscle-cell dissolution; they are therefore secondary.

The intestinal wall thus appears to be a dividing area between two completely different kinds of worlds, a place where significant events occur.

To understand them, we will need to turn our attention to processes taking place outside man in nature.

In *The Nature of Substance* I made an exhaustive study of the nature and life of plants. Data gathered in the course of long years of experimentation were presented there, attesting to the appearance and later disappearance of both plant and mineral substances. Seedlings enclosed in airtight glass containers showed a gain in weight as substance came into being, and then lost weight again at certain intervals as matter passed over into an imponderable state (Fig. 3). This waxing and waning of substances took place in consonance with rhythms of the sun and moon. Complete analyses of seeds and of plants grown from them in distilled water brought to light a rhythmic pattern in which mineral substances too (potash, calcium, magnesium, silica and sulphur) came into being and passed away again. So the belief that existence originated out of matter has to be countered by the view that a spiritual cosmos continually brings forth the visible world and again withdraws it into immaterial forms of being. Life that was the product of an already existent spiritual world was present long

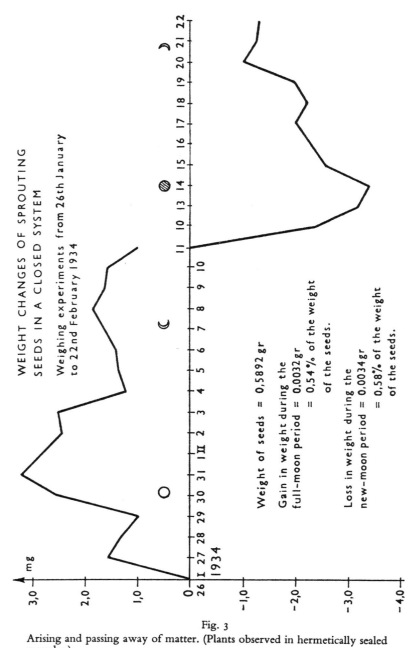

Fig. 3

Arising and passing away of matter. (Plants observed in hermetically sealed ampules.)

before matter was manifested. The dogma of the pre-existence of matter must be opposed by the idea of the pre-existence of the spirit.

Matter is creation's last stage of precipitation, and only where its descent has taken it out and beyond the realm of life is it subject to the mechanical and chemical laws governing the mineral kingdom. We are too prone to project these laws into the living kingdoms and even out into universal space, letting an erroneous picture of the world persist for centuries. Currently recognized physical and chemical laws obtain only in the inorganic sphere. Wherever life lays hold on lifeless matter, mass, weight and number are no longer sole criteria; cosmic laws of metamorphosis (polarity and – to use the Goethean term – intensification) start to operate. In the plant world, where, as Goethe says in *Faust*, Scene II,

> The heavenly forces up and down are ranging,
> Ever their golden treasure interchanging,

the cosmos has its own living laws and rhythms, according to which it organizes matter and guides it through changing forms of being, right up to the immaterial condition of a 'heavenly force' and back again into dense material forms susceptible of being weighed and analysed.

'The plant is not the product of the soil, but the soil rather the product of the plant,' writes Herzeele in *The Origin of Inorganic Substances* (Berlin, 1876). 'Where calcium and magnesium are found, a plant must have lived and deposited these substances.'

Light, air and water create the rainbow. Plants create the substance in their green leaves by assimilating the same elements: light, air (carbonic acid) and water.* The chemical formula of this sublime process:

$$6CO_2 + 5H_2O = C_6H_{10}O_5 + 6O_2$$

makes one think of a rattling skeleton long bereft of any trace of life.

Moreover, the formula does not include light, the very element that makes assimilation possible. Only a rainbow background affords this process proper life and character.

* Cf. *The Nature of Substance*, p. 22.

The starch found in the plant's green middle zone hardens lower down where it comes under the influence of earth forces and becomes cellulose, with its woody permanence of form; while under the sun's influence it changes on its upward climb into the finer element of sugar. The etherealizing of substance continues sunward through the stages of nectar, the fragrance of etheric oils, pollen-dust, and brilliant blossom colouring. As the season advances the plant blooms, falls and is reduced to dust as it dematerializes, so to speak into the universe. As Goethe might have said: when the substantial plant decays, its being – the living idea which brings it forth – returns to the outermost reaches of the cosmos. The mineral-like seed which remains is only an anchorhold by means of which the being of the plant finds its way back into the world of appearances when conditions warrant. In spring, when nature sprouts, shoots and buds, the idea of the plant starts incarnating, reaching the peak of its visible existence about the middle of the year. In summer plants bloom, fade and begin to dry. By autumn only the seed is left; the being of the plant has withdrawn from sight, to reappear in the following spring from the seed.

This mighty rhythm linking being and appearance embraces those smaller rhythms of contraction and expansion found in the metamorphoses of leaves. These rhythms are always accompanied by metamorphoses of form and substance.

As we study the plant with our eye sensitive to the facts before us, it teaches us to abandon our modern concepts of indestructible matter based on the materialistic, mechanical views of atomic and molecular chemistry. For plants clearly demonstrate the fact that matter is just a fixed stage of universal processes. What earthlings call substance is cosmic activity in dense, arrested form. Earthly materiality and cosmic being are two opposite poles between which Nature's span appears in infinitely many stages. Plants are living links between the poles of the world organism.

To return to digestion: What happens to the liquid chyme on the other side of the intestinal wall?

Would it not strike the reader as absurd to imagine a plant that had spent itself in perfume and radiance and then had finally crumbled into dust coming to material re-synthesis out in the universe beyond earth's atmosphere? The plant's continuance in the cosmos is far more purely spiritual. The whole universe is involved in its re-entering the visible world at germination; macrocosmic processes condense themselves into the substance of the plant.

The etherealization of the chyme as it passes the intestinal wall and enters upon the first, completely non-material phase, is perfectly analogous. The nutrient substances fade away as it were into the inner metabolic organism. And just as the cosmos brings forth a visible, substantial plant when it acts on the material anchor-hold of the seed, so man creates his own human substance (complete human protein) out of equally non-material phases of nutrient substances through the agency of his digestive organs.

Then is man in fact a microcosm complete with all those elements recognized as creative forces in external nature?

This is a question best considered in the light of animal development.

Plants come into physical existence as a direct result of the interaction of cosmic forces. Animals exhibit a quite different developmental impulse: they detach a part of their surroundings and make it into a world of their own, a place for the development of internal organs.*

The growth of an animal from a fertilized egg is, to start with, a purely vegetative process. Through cell division, a mass of cells known as the morula comes into being. This soon takes on the sphere-form of the blastula. But then something entirely new makes its appearance: the blastula turns in upon itself, assuming a bowl-like shape, with a depression which grows deeper and deeper, until, at the gastrula stage, an interior is completely sheathed off from an exterior world. This is an essential characteristic of animal maturation, which is analogous to that of plants only up to the moment when the gastrula is formed. The forming of the gastrula marks a turn in a new direction. This organ is the basic form of animal development and the ancestral pattern of every multicellular creature.

The inner surface (the entoderm) produced by this turning in upon itself of the embryo is the primal structure out of which the

* Cf. *The Nature of Substance*, p. 78.

internal organs of animals eventually develop. The outer surface (the ectoderm) serves as the foundation for the nerves and senses. Animals thus come to possess both inner and outer worlds – an entirely new principle, which represents a decided advance over the vegetative.

The plant lives in the element of cosmic light. It is formed by macrocosmic influences and extends out to the starry universe. So plants may be said to originate from far beyond the earth. Their function is that of carriers of life (oxygen); of life which comes into earthly form as carbon and passes away again as hydrogen, a fire-related substance and as such most nearly cosmic. Starch (carbohydrate) is thus the true plant substance.

A totally different process is at work building the animal organism, for animals, as sensate creatures capable of locomotion, are possessors of what is called a soul. Sensation is actually movement on a higher level, movement of the soul. It is therefore not enough for nitrogen (air substance) to work on the organism only from without. The basic tendency must be toward intensification of the inner element for the animal form as a whole to be capable of independent movement in which the cosmos plays no part. So animals may be said to have made a portion of the creative universe their inner possession and to have built themselves systems of internal organs, developing hearts, lungs, livers, etc. The carbohydrates developed by plants as their particular building material are the product of direct cosmic radiation and external light, whereas the production of proteins in the animal body takes place inside it and is the result of turning the cosmos 'outside in'. Systems of internal organs are simply inversions of extra-terrestrial processes and forces, focal centres of an in-turned universe.

The great range and variety of animal forms stem from the fact that each species represents only one small part of the formative forces of the universe, which it inverts. Animals are invariably one-sided developments. They lack the harmonizing force macrocosmically represented by the sun. But this is compensated for by the perfection of their bodily capacities, which man by no means shares. Who, for example, would think of trying to outswim a fish or expect to improve on the strength and elasticity of a lion's spring? Wise men of old had good reason to give the constellations animal names and to call their circle the 'zodiac', for they are the source of the formative impulses shaping the animal kingdom. Inverted, each constellation gives the impetus for some particular form-development. This explains the variety of types and species.

But an entirely new element, harmony, appears on the scene with the human creature. Man the microcosm is all-embracing. In him all the formative principles of the animal kingdom are present in the harmonious shaping of the human form. He is not the product of a single constellation, but of all twelve, and of the planets and the sun as well. He is therefore endowed with more than just the capacities for independent movement and sensation which he has in common with the animal: he is a personality. The sun orders and rules the universe, and man's ego may be thought of as the spiritual sun of his entelechy, the seat of reason and enlightened judgment, the true centre of his total body, soul and spiritual being.

With his ego man is joined to the stream of spiritual evolution.

Now, what actually happens when a human being digests his food?

The foodstuffs fade, as it were, from the intestinal tract over into the microcosmic space of man. Just as the sun causes plants to spring up, blossom, pour out their fragrance and again decay, so a man applies the strength of his personality to breaking down and gradually translating his nutriment into the non-material field of force that occupies man the microcosm. And exactly as the sun, representing the cosmos, brings forth the new plant and its substances, so does the ego in control of the human micro-organism and its forces create its own body-building protein. Complete human protein is precipitated from man's microcosmic substance by his human complex of forces much as a sunny summer afternoon clouds over and a thunderstorm releases showers of rain from the lowering skies. The details of this process will be discussed below.

Digestion is thus a spiritualizing of matter and a stimulating of the forces of personality to the creation of new human substance.

But it follows from this that digestion is a capacity of personality.

It is therefore always an individual process, as individual as the bodily substances which it precipitates. No two human beings are ever found to possess identical blood, for example. Everybody knows that two individuals fed exactly alike develop quite differently. One is easily satiated, the other always hungry; one is healthy, the other ailing; one is fat, the other thin; one is smart, the other simple. Reason enough to steer clear of dogmatism in matters nutritional!

In earlier times people had a healthy instinct for what did them good. Long ago, when group-soul ties still united them, priests and leaders in the Mysteries were their guides in nutrition as in other matters. Now the time is ripe for guidance and instinct to be replaced by knowledge. But a striving for knowledge exposes the seeker to error on the one hand, to dogmatism on the other. This explains why chaos reigns in knowledge – and nutrition – at the present time. In what is to follow, the various foodstuffs will be characterized in a way to enable everyone to recognize the nature of those forces in his environment with which he must come to grips nutritionally. Then a nutritional regime suited to an individual's needs can be evolved from the basic facts set forth. To follow this course takes the ground from under fanaticism, which can flourish only in the presence of a limited and hence distorting viewpoint.

CHAPTER THREE

The History of Human Nutrition

The idea that man's nutritional customs have scarcely changed since human life began is as wrong as the assumption that he has always been related to the world about him with the same type of consciousness.

In an earlier chapter we pointed out the polarity between the life of the senses and the metabolism, and showed how both could be understood as metamorphoses of breathing: the sense life as a process moving upward toward increasing refinement, the metabolism as a downward coarsening. Sensation and digestion are almost undifferentiated in the middle zone of the breath, where they are found in *statu nascendi*. This is apparent in the case of feeling, in the breath's tendency to speed up or slow down according to how some emotional experience affects us. The opposite is illustrated by the way we 'drink in the winey air' like a refreshing draught and have a sense of being nourished by its 'spiciness'. The difference between the two processes at this stage is very slight indeed.

The upward refining process, then, builds up the physical basis of the wide-awake nerve and sense organism, while the opposite downward, coarsening process serves the completely unconscious digestive functions.

It is not surprising that these polar processes should go parallel with human evolution as it changes and reaches ever more highly developed stages. If digestion is indeed a capacity of the ego, tracing the ego's development gives a clue to man's changing habits of nutrition. The human spirit gradually lays hold on itself and on the world. Since foods are part of the world, it lays hold on these too, and in digesting learns to digest the world.

The development of consciousness in mankind as a whole has been piecemeal and tortuous. Still, the great primal rhythms weave their patterns in it ever and again, and so too in nutrition. Single forward steps were made here and there, creating a colourful tapestry of varying nutritional habits. Next to a progressive development one would find outdated ways and customs lingering on. This makes for the rich variety of conservative and progressive elements found in all living processes. A study of civilizations cleárly shows these great steps or rhythms in man's changing habits of nutrition.

Let us trace these, going back as far as there is documentation. We can begin with the early civilization of India, which followed upon the great catastrophe known in the legends of many peoples as the Flood. It was the period recorded in the Vedas, though these like other mythological records were written much later.

The Vedas have much of interest and significance to say about nutrition. The Indians of antiquity raised animals in order to have their milk as food.

Milk is the earliest of human foods. It is the product of living, sentient organisms, whose organs of lactation are part of the reproductive system. Reproduction is subject to moon rhythms, the menses. Milk is therefore also connected with the moon principle. It contains everything a growing organism needs and is a complete food, a liquid synthesis of protein, fat, carbohydrates and mineral salts. All the building materials of the animal, vegetable and mineral kingdoms are contained in milk as though in embryo.

We may say, then, that ancient humanity lived chiefly on animal products. This form of nutrition dates back to the time before the Flood and continues as one of the sources of man's nutriment.

According to what spiritual science has to tell us, milk is connected with the moon principle, and, as we showed above, is part of the reproductive process. Spiritual science reports that the moon principle completely permeated the earth in those ancient times when the two cosmic bodies were still a single entity. The atmosphere of this planet was suffused with a milky, egg-white-like substance which the totally different living creatures of the period absorbed as food. Only later, when the moon had separated from the earth, did organs of lactation form inside the body as part of the reproductive system.

The moon is that region of the cosmos from which issue the forces responsible for the reproductive capacity. I went fully into this in *The Nature of Substance* in the chapter on silver, showing how this metal can be called the earthly representative of moon forces, with special reference to reproduction. These same moon forces are active in the vegetable kingdom as the cosmic force of germination. They are found again in a metamorphosed, involuted, interiorized form in the reproductive capacity and organs of man and animals. This fact is reflected in the moon-rhythm of the human reproductive organism, despite man's emancipation from cosmic influences.

Milk, then, is the original, earliest form of nourishment. We note that cattle, still held sacred in India today, have always played an important rôle in Indian mythology. It might be proper to call this phase 'nutritional antiquity'.

The Persian civilization, which followed the Indian, brought a radically new trend in nutrition. Zarathustra, who was looked on as the teacher throughout the entire period, taught his people how to grow those plants which are still our most important food sources. The fruits and grains we grow today all spring from the rose and lily families and stem from the profound occult cosmic knowledge of the 'Wise men of the Orient'. There have been no essentially new plant-breeding developments since that time. The Zend Avesta can claim to be the first agricultural textbook.

Fruits and vegetables now came to play the chief rôle in nutrition. Food was a sun-product. The nutritional epoch that began with this development has many phases, which will be examined in detail below.

It was not so very long ago that still another element entered the picture: At about the time of Christ, civilized peoples began to crave salted food. Feuds raged over the possession of salt springs and deposits. Salt began to seem a necessity of life. And though today many authorities question whether this is well-founded, we will see that the use of salt was a natural step ahead in evolution. For mankind was on the threshold of a new phase of development in which minerals are also foods. With it, nutrition took on a truly earthy character.

This may seem paradoxical. And we certainly do not mean that stones are about to become our bread. The term 'mineral' must be understood here in its widest application as indicative of the recent trend of civilization. This would include the devitalization to which plant and animal foods are subjected by being cooked, preserved, and so on. When certain nomadic peoples were no longer content with just drinking the milk of their animals, but killed and ate them, and when we go further and boil or roast and then salt our meat, this all tends in a deadening, mineralizing direction.

Returning to a consideration of the plant as the second and therefore middle phase of nutritional evolution, we find it occupying a middle position between animal and mineral in still another sense. For the root that forms one pole of the plant is closely related to the mineral earth; it is salty and bitter. The opposite pole, the butterfly-like blossom, is related to the animate sphere of insect life; here it develops sweet nectars and the juiciness of fruits.

Plants fit into the picture of nutritional history in a further dimension: it was the parts above the earth that man first used for food; honey has a relationship with milk. Only much later were roots used as foods, forming a bridge over to the mineral phase. Beet sugar has something in common with salt, not in a chemical sense, but in the above extension of the concept of minerality. It is a root substance, which has undergone much cooking and refining and, in the end product, come out in the crystalline form characteristic of minerals.

There are, then, three distinct major nutritional phases: an early period, during which animals were man's chief food source; a middle age, when plant products came to be included in his diet, and, finally, the present period, only just begun, in which minerals begin to figure prominently.

Now what is the significance of this step by step nutritional relationship to the kingdoms of nature that developed through the ages?

What do we find running parallel to it in the history of developing human consciousness?

One cannot escape the conclusion that earth dwellers of the time described as nutritional antiquity had a totally different consciousness from that of present day humanity. They had no intellectual capacity whatever, but possessed instead the power to perceive a world beyond the senses. This was the period before the Vedas, when the ancient Aryans brought the first culture down into India from the mountains of Central Asia. In those days the spiritual world and its inhabitants were as real to people as our physical surroundings are to us today; it was, indeed, the whole of reality, while the world of nature was felt to be unreal, 'Maya', or illusion, the lowest level of creation. And these ancient Indians were not conscious of themselves as we are today. They felt wholly one with the gods; each was an instrument through which the divine breath pulsated. This period was later recorded in the Vedas. One gathers that personal freedom was then unknown. Individuals could not have formed judgments and then made their own decisions. Rather did they feel supported and guided by spiritual beings. Their souls were 'in the lap of the gods', their personalities childlike and undeveloped.

The middle periods that followed were characterized by an awakening interest in the earth and nature. But this descent into the material world was very slow and gradual. Thus an awakening interest in the earth led the ancient Persians to begin developing the first rudiments of agriculture. But as interest in things of earth quickened, contact with the spiritual world grew dimmer, despite the fact that, by modern standards, it would still have seemed very vivid. And it still continued to be the decisive guide for human action.

As time went on, however, only a few specially placed individuals such as the Egyptian priest-kings were still capable of perceiving and acting upon divine guidance; clairvoyance gradually ebbed away, even for the Greek initiates. Hand in hand with this development went a strengthening of individual capacity, prone, of course, to every kind of error.

All mythologies picture this evolutionary step, the Cain-Abel legend perhaps most impressively. Cain and Abel make a sacrifice to God. Abel is described as a man pleasing in God's sight; he is a shepherd, whose food is furnished by his animals. Cain is not close to God, as Abel is, for he has become a distinct personality. He is a tiller of the soil and an eater of fruits and vegetables. God accepts the sacrifice of Abel, who is still a mere instrument of the divine will and can therefore do no wrong. But Cain makes up his own mind, and is therefore subject to all possible error. His sacrifice is rejected, and he kills Abel. The story is an impressive picturing of the connection that links death and killing with being separated from God and becoming an independent ego. If we allow the whole picture to work on us, we feel how accurately it symbolizes the victory of a new, progressive, state of consciousness over an old, outworn condition, and the price – guilt and error – that must be paid for it.

Surveying this development, we find evidence that divine forces that once approached man from a spiritual world outside him were metamorphosed into capacities evolving within the human soul, capacities which man had to learn to handle on his own. The same process described in the first chapter from the physiological angle – gastrulation, or the interiorization of the cosmos into a system of internal organs – here takes place on the psychological level as an internalizing of powers of the soul. Macrocosmic forces long experienced as divinities who worked on and through man in the course of evolution became, as it were, inverted, absorbed into the interior of the soul. The highest of these forces is the inner sun of the microcosmic human ego, which has the function of harmonizing processes on all other levels, physiological, psychological and spiritual.

This process of gradual interiorization, the ever fuller incarnating of the ego, belongs to the period characterized above as modern. Man becomes increasingly free of the spiritual world and spiritual guidance, though he can find them again within himself if he makes the effort.

Egoism and materialism are necessary stages of this development. Greek philosophy entered the phase of logical-conceptual thinking with Aristotle, and in the course of the centuries this became modern abstract intellectuality. Thinking thus deserted the realm of essential being to become a shrunken shadow of itself, mere reflection; it grew 'root-like' and 'salty'. The qualitative was submerged by the quantitative. A universe which Kepler and Copernicus still believed was a living organism became a burned-out slagheap to those who came after them. Only when the ego has come to know itself and its origin in the spirit will civilization be revivified. German Idealism took the first steps in this direction with Fichte, Schelling and Hegel. Goethe and Novalis gave it world-wide dimensions. Rudolf Steiner's Anthroposophy brought it final perfection. Egoism will be overcome by those who travel this path, for the ego will give birth to something higher than its own small personal self. An ego that has interiorized the divinely ordered universe will have a true perspective on the material world. It will imprint its own spirit on the world and thus transform it.

Now what does all this have to do with nutritional considerations?

We recall that digesting is a function of the ego. The forces of personality are to the body what the sun is to the plant world. Just as the sun governs the plant's cycle of blooming and etherealization and is able to create new plants with all their various substances so ego forces use intestinal fermentation processes to break down and gradually etherealize the nutritional stream into a non-material condition, out of which they then recreate original human substance.

If this is true, it is easy to understand why an ego not as yet fully present in an organism is too weak to digest anything but milk, that it takes a stronger ego force to digest vegetables, and that our egos have only very recently developed to the point of being able to digest minerals. For minerals occupy the lowest level of organization of the kingdoms of Nature. They are dead; they have nothing but shape. Plants are more highly organized; they possess life as well as form. Animals rise one step higher through the sentience and motility present in their living forms. And man, Nature's peak, permeates form, life and feeling with the highest principle, the ego, the thinking spirit.

When man eats animal products, the ego has to lift these animal substances one step higher, to the human level. Such foods as milk and milk-products, eggs and meat are easiest to digest, especially when eaten raw.

Plant foods must be lifted two steps higher to be tolerated by organisms functioning on the human level. More ego power is needed here. Vegetarian foods are therefore harder to digest than animal foods.

Minerals are the least digestible, for they must be raised three levels above their native stage of organization. Only well developed personalities are strong enough to deal with these dead substances, i.e., to lay hold on the realm of earth.

In the light of these facts the parallel development of consciousness and nutrition becomes perfectly clear. For the history of developing consciousness is necessarily the history of the ego.

For each individual there is a repetition of the development which took place for the entire human race in a time-span covering centuries and millennia. Each personal nutritional history begins with the milk drinking phase of infancy, goes on to include scraped raw apples, spinach and other vegetables and cereals, and then reaches the stage of being able to digest spiced and salted foods. Careful observers will notice that a desire for salt and spicy flavouring usually makes its appearance at the age when personality is beginning to come out strongly in young people.

The mother's milk on which a baby lives is human substance, simply transferred to his organism. It is the proper food for him in that it makes the least demands on his digestion. This stage is comparable to the earliest phase of man's nutritional evolution, when living organisms lay as it were at the bosom of nature, the great mother, and drank in earth's albumen-impregnated atmosphere.

For the sake of avoiding misconceptions here, let it be said that we are not making value judgments in calling a weak ego the cause of a weak digestion. It is perfectly possible to be a highly-developed nature and yet have poor digestive powers, because the ego forces are called upon for labours in other parts of the organism, and are too little concerned with digestion. And just the opposite is often true: an insignificant person can have a strong digestion as a result of devoting all his ego strength to his metabolism. Keeping a harmonious balance in the use of one's forces is a matter of healing and development, of establishing the right connection between body and spirit, of just the right degree of incarnation. Nutritional history can therefore also be read as the descent of human spirits into bodies for the sake of strengthening the spirit's transubstantiative powers.

CHAPTER FOUR

Cosmic Nutrition

M an is related in a twofold way to the spatial world in which he lives: through his metabolic processes and through his senses. The first is a physical connection, the second spiritual.

In accordance with custom, we called the connection with his surroundings which man's metabolism gives him 'nutrition', and termed the substances that undergo metabolic transformation into human substance 'food'. As these latter pass through the stomach and intestines, they are reduced to their most elementary form. They thereupon disappear through the intestinal wall and are spiritualized, only to be re-precipitated as human protein. This we will term the *earthly* stream of nutrition.

The excretory processes must be reckoned part of this stream. Present day physiology sees them merely as waste-product removal systems. There is another and more realistic view that sees in them other, more important functions. Perhaps a comparison with a natural process outside man's organism will serve to clarify what we have in mind.

We can make a solution of colloidal silver, which is a dark brown or almost black liquid, clean it by dialysis and let it separate into flakes. The dark solution curdles, and after the black coagulation-product settles there is a clear transparent fluid at the top, which can be filtered off. It is pure water, without any chemical trace of silver whatsoever. But biological tests show it to have properties of potentialized silver. We know that the higher homoeopathic potencies are not based on the material presence of a given substance; they are, rather, energies inherent in that substance at a higher, immaterial level. Homoeopathic dilutions are made by protracted rhythmical thinning and shaking, which causes the physical substance gradually to disappear, while an immaterial spiritual energy called a potency emerges in its place. In the above-mentioned case, however, all the silver is separated out at once, in what may be called an excretory process. It is like pumping, in that downward pressure on the pump handle creates a vacuum that matches the depletion with a fresh intake.

26

Something quite similar happens with excretion in the metabolic system. Everyone must have noticed how lively the conscious functions are when excretion is normal, and conversely, how paralyzed thought, will and feeling become when one is 'constipated' in the broadest sense. Perception and consciousness are dulled, for a lazy metabolism means that the nerves serving the senses cannot function properly. We see here how related the upper and lower parts of the organism are and how they reflect and affect one another – a subject to be elaborated in a further chapter.

Our senses enable us to have an interchange with our surroundings. What we see, hear, smell, taste and touch becomes the basis of our concepts. Thinking works on these and builds them into an orderly structure of ideas and ideals. These are taken up by the will as we try to realize them in the various forms of artistic, scientific and professional activity. Thus we enter into life and make our mark.

All this has a far closer tie-up with the cosmic order than one might suppose.

We have studied plants and seen how they are caught up in a rhythmic alteration between bodily appearance and a state of disembodied being. Thanks to this alternation, their visible beauty rejoices us in the summertime, while in autumn they pour themselves out and stream away into the invisible realm of pure being in dissipating clouds of fragrance and colour. We know that the idea of the plant, which the seed anchored, returns to manifestation every following spring. Though this may seem just a picture, living with it brings us the experience that Goethe had. He actually perceived the plant's primal being and would not accept Schiller's suggestion that all he saw was 'a mere idea'. The cosmos is full of such ideas, endowed with real being, and each least one is a thought of God. God's thinking has indeed become outer nature, become a visible universe.

How can we enter into such a concept and make it our own most intimate experience?

Sometimes we carry a thought about with us for years on end. At first it may be too unformed for expression, and we cannot seem to get a firm hold on it. Little by little, however, it takes on shape and clarity. It has solidified to the point where it can be expressed and written down, or communicated in some other visible artistic medium. This makes us creators of a visible realm, that of art. Can we conceive of nature and the universe having come into being in any other manner? Must the macrocosm not be governed by an activity analogous to human thinking but of a loftier and far more all-embracing kind, which creates all the manifold variety of forms in nature? Nature and art may be compared to an object and its reflection in a mirror! A work of art is real to the degree that it reflects a universal truth. A culture may be said to fulfil its mission when the works of men wear the lustre of universal thought.

Like human thoughts that have been bodied forth in works of art and then find resurrection in the minds of those who see and understand them, universal thoughts celebrate resurrection in us when we approach nature's creation with open minds and senses. *And this is the cosmic nutritive stream.* Impressions and perceptions of the world about us flow continuously into us through all our senses. This stream consists of upbuilding forces, the very same forces that come from the periphery of the cosmos and create the various species of plants. They are the same forces that build up the human organism and become its very flesh and blood. Our perceptive life is actually participation in the life of the whole universe, though we are no longer conscious of it. The world of nature which lies spread out before our senses is the product of divine activity, the very same activity that made our bodies. These bodies are actually microcosmic copies of the universe.

In the previous chapter we described how, little by little, human beings lost touch with cosmic reality, becoming free individuals at the expense of their spiritual connection with the universe. This had the effect of hardening the body. In earlier times man's intercourse with a God-filled world made him the recipient of forces that kept him physically far more plastic. Today he is on his own in a God-less world and must think and feel and will his groping way back to the creative forces of the universe as a free spirit.

Human thinking, human will and human feeling can, if they make the necessary effort, find the way to a new harmony with divine creative thinking, re-experiencing cosmic thoughts in full participation. Achieving this to some degree or other activates recreative forces in our organisms. Failure to attain it leaves our thinking abstract and unreal, just something made up by the brain, and has a breaking-down effect, for then we lack contact with the nourishing formative forces of the cosmos. People in this category like to talk of not having to bother with eating, and instead swallowing a few pills that are chemically equivalent. Their ideal is to stay perfectly passive, to save time, to avoid coming to grips with earth and cosmos in the ways which are required if they are to be adequately nourished. Body and soul would both dry up, under such a régime, the body becoming sclerotic, the soul joyless and incapable of interest. The term 'uplift' suggests something of the element required. We all know how nourished we feel when we have entertained great thoughts or experienced the beauty and wisdom to be found in art and nature. Some may even have noticed how little interest they feel in material food when on a mountain climb, especially up among the high peaks.

In one of his books, the novelist Rudolf Hans Bartsch describes the meal of a person with sensitive feeling for the world of nature. It is a delight to read how he sits at table eating bread and vegetables while he contemplates the ways of the airy element, the streaming down of fructifying rain, the roughness of ploughed fields, the sun's capacity to ripen things. He rejoices in the apple's roundness, the glorious array of colour in his fruit bowl, the pretty crockery, the clean white tablecloth. These pleasurable thoughts awaken his deepest gratitude and love. A ceremonial mood enwraps the scene, and the writer calls it a 'feast of embodiment'. He would have us realize that being fed involves both the spirit and the body, that it is communion between heaven and earth celebrated by and in human beings.

The following considerations may help to clarify the way the earthly and cosmic nutritional streams work into one another.

We compared the earthly nutritional stream with a plant growing from above downward, undergoing progressive etherealization until it finally disappears through the intestinal wall and into the blood. The process of digestion subjects food in its original coarse form to a gradual breakdown. First, it is mechanically reduced by chewing, then chemically reduced by its passage through the stomach and intestinal tract. Carbohydrates are changed to sugars, fats to glycerine and fatty acids, the product finally etherealizing over into the spiritual microcosm through the intestinal wall. And just as the cosmos responded to the plant's etherealization by producing seed, so human protein is precipitated on the far side of the intestinal wall.

And what, we may ask, constitutes the seed of this reversed plant?

Earthly food goes to nourish the nervous system in particular. Observation in starvation areas of Central Europe give all necessary confirmation of this fact. Malnutrition first shows itself in nerve-sense degeneration, symptomized by forgetfulness, nervous depletion, inability to think, and so on, to disturbances of sight and hearing. Later, of course, the damage spreads to the whole organism, for the nervous system as a whole is 'trophic'. So we have to conceive the 'seed' of the etherealized stream of nutriment as consisting of the activity of nerves and senses.

Now what does a seed do when planted in a fertile soil?

It puts forth roots and produces a new plant. And our nerves and senses do exactly this. They reach out as with roots into the universe to perceive and so partake of the spiritual sustenance it offers in the form of creative forces proceeding from the thoughts of divinity, thus enabling a new 'plant' to grow up in us. This plant is a reversed one also. It grows downward, out of spirit into matter, condensing its stream of supersensible, non-material energy quite literally into flesh and blood.

It might be objected that some people seem to get along without a cosmic nutritional stream in that they never give a single thought to universal truth. And certainly this can be the case for quite some time, with no obvious evidence of severe illness and degeneration. This is the case, however, only because no one is in fact wholly shut off from all participation in a larger life. It is true, nevertheless, that the quality of such a person's bodily substance is very different from that of a person who relates in a loving way to the world around him.

Where the cosmic nutritional stream dries up, the organism

tries to make up for it by demanding an increase in the earthly stream. One therefore finds that people whose habitual attitude is antipathetic (this would include abstract thinkers and people chained to a desk by their professions) have poor digestions. They can eat and still not feel satisfied. Those who become part of their surroundings through the strength of their empathy require less material nutriment.

The author had an interesting experience of this while teaching. In a nutrition course that touched on cosmic nutrition during the period of greatest dietary deprivation in Germany, a locksmith's apprentice raised his hand and said: 'Now I see why my mother keeps strong and well in spite of eating almost nothing. She's a very kind-hearted person, and always puts her bread on my father's plate. Now I realize that the bread she gives my father nourishes her better than it does him.'

It is equally possible to show that some human beings can live without the *earthly* nutritional stream. Lives of certain saints are an example, particularly the phenomenal case that startled the whole scientific world a few decades ago: that of Theresa Neumann of Konnersreuth.

Theresa Neumann was a Franconian peasant child who grew up quite normally on her parents' farm. She was a deeply religious tender-hearted little girl. One day she fell from a ladder escaping from a fire and was bedridden. With these unusual events she began to live an abnormal life, which earned her the reputation of a saint. She refused to take any nourishment except the Host, the consecrated wafer which she took at communion. Every week she lived through the crucifixion of Jesus Christ in a state of diminished waking consciousness, and on Fridays the stigmata appeared on her hands and feet, causing heavy bleeding. At such times she often spoke fluent Aramaic and seemed to be pleading with someone. She lived many years in this condition despite repeated serious loss of blood and the lack of any earthly food worthy of the name. Physicians, scientists and other trustworthy persons looked into the matter and found it as described. Since orthodox science had no explanation, the case was quietly dropped. What really took place was an activation of the cosmic nutritional stream under the influence of Theresa's experience of the greatest events of human and spiritual history – an activation powerful enough to sustain bodily life without any physical nourishment whatever.

Pondering such matters, one comes to understand the complicated nutritional processes described by Rudolf Steiner in lectures to doctors and which might be summed up as follows: Earthly nutriment works chiefly on the nerve-sense organs, whereas cosmic nutriment maintains the digestive organs which are built up by the blood. *The metabolic organs consist of cosmic substance but serve the earthly nutritional stream; the nerve-sense system is made of earthly substance but serves cosmic nutrition.*

These statements are borne out by experiments made by the author in the laboratories of the Clinical-Therapeutic Institute at Arlesheim near Basel from 1929 to 1932.

These experiments used wheat seedlings as the biological reagent. Seeds were selected with a view to uniformity and well-developed, healthy form. Ten such seeds were put in plates filled with distilled water. They floated on the surface until they germinated and sent down roots. Their growth was then observed and measured.

Wheat seedlings developing in this way provide such a sensitive testing medium that both growth-encouraging and growth-inhibiting forces show up plainly. Substances derived from both metabolic and nerve-sense organs were tested for their influence on growth, in an arrangement based on the characteristic way each works. This meant that the possible direct effects of the organ substances had to be allowed for as well as the possibility of radiation from the circumference. In the first case, grains of wheat were sprouted directly in dilute solutions of matter taken from the various organs instead of distilled water. In the second, distilled water was used, but the sealed plate in which the seeds were planted was set inside another jar containing a solution of matter from the same organ; the seeds were thus exposed to radiation from the enclosing sphere. In the first case, the seedling could absorb the substance in the solution directly, while in the second they were merely exposed to its radiation-influence.

The organs used were taken from a calf a few moments after slaughtering.

It might be objected that animal digestion cannot be compared with that of human beings, since animals have no ego. Nevertheless, the experiments do indicate the basic nature of the processes involved.

A series of tests was carried out using substances from the brain,

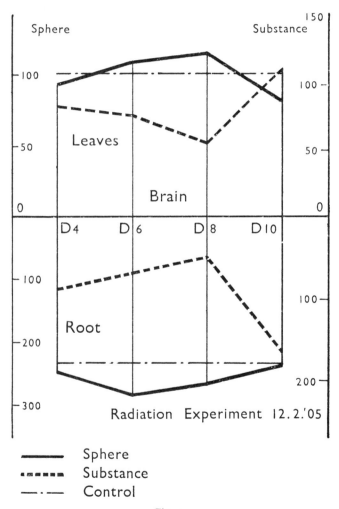

Fig. 4

Observation of wheat shoots in solutions of organ substances and in their spheres of radiation.

33

iris, retina, the choroid membrane of the eye, and the vitreous humour, all organs of the nerve-sense system. In the metabolic-organ tests spleen and ovarian matter were used. Solutions were made in various dilutions, the tests being made with the fourth, sixth, eighth and tenth potencies. The method of preparing these potencies was described in *The Nature of Substance*, in the chapter on 'High Dilutions and Their Effects'.

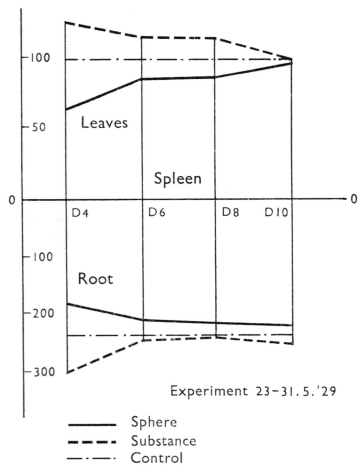

Experiment 23–31.5.'29

———— Sphere

━ ━ ━ ▪ Substance

—·—· Control

Fig. 5

Observation of wheat shoots in dilute solutions of spleen substances and in their spheres of radiation.

The experiments were brought to an end after ten days, where-upon the length of roots and leaves was measured and averaged. Figures 4, 5 and 6 show the resulting curves. The average leaf length appears above the line, the root length below it.

It was clearly shown that nerve-sense substances promote growth when rayed in from a surrounding sphere. They not only radiate their own forces, but are transmitters of peripheral radiation. But in direct substantial application they proved useless. The derivatives of the metabolic organs, however, were taken up and used by the seedlings, but showed no radiation influence.

The two nutritional streams thus merge from above and below into a full circle of cosmic and terrestrial relatedness.

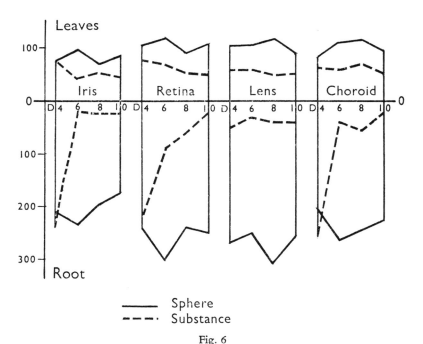

Fig. 6

Observation of plants in dilute solutions of eye substances and in their spheres of radiation.

CHAPTER FIVE

Formation of Protein by the Organs

Carbohydrates are the material from which plants are built. They can be broken down into charcoal and water, as happens when a leaf or flower or a piece of wood is heated in a test tube. Water droplets form on the inside of the tube, and there is a solid residue of carbon shaped just like the plant. This is the reason why the plant building material was called carbohydrate. We know too that water can in turn be broken down into hydrogen and oxygen, so that plants can be said to consist of three elements: carbon, hydrogen and oxygen. But we should not think of these as building stones, for it is impossible to make a carbohydrate out of carbon, hydrogen and oxygen. The elements in question are breakdown products, corpses as it were of a once living substance, reminders of the life that once flourished there.

The black, skeletal substance carbon is not, then, the building matter of the plant kingdom; another aspect of carbon – its cosmic aspect as a universal shaping force – weaves the living fabric of the plant kingdom out of the surroundings of the earth. Wherever form predominates in plant life, as in the veining found in leaf and blossom, or in the woody structure of stalk and root, there carbon is the dominant force, the bearer of the cosmos' shaping power, the element that fixes life in earthly patterns. It manifests this characteristic even as a physical substance in its readiness to combine with itself and make the complex chains and rings that are the basis of organic compounds. The formulae of structural chemistry clearly picture this formative capacity. The shaping process is not, however, inherent in the substance carbon: material carbon is simply its last and most substantial product. It is the agent that forms starch and converts it into cellulose. But its presence can be materially ascertained only after the destruction of the plant. Substance is the final step in cosmic process.

Carbon's capacity for introducing fixed framework patternings into living processes, to shape what is coming into earthly manifestation, tells us that it is *the* earth-substance par excellence.

If, however, we turn our attention to material hydrogen and look with equally intuitive perception for the process indwelling in the substance, we find it to be the etherealizing force of cosmic fire. Hydrogen is known to be the earth's lightest substance, and we can study its buoyancy exhaustively in physical and chemical phenomena. Also connected with this is its close relationship to fire, which persuaded the author to change its name from hydrogen (in German 'water substance') to 'fire-substance' in his earlier book, *The Nature of Substance*. It is this etherealizing fire as cosmic process that makes plants unfold, bloom, expend all their wealth of colour and fragrance and waste away to the point of final dissolution. Cosmic fire de-materializes plants and burns them up, leaving only the tiny seed as residue. Cosmic fire is also active in the forming of starches and in their etherealization into sugar form. But here again, hydrogen can be proved materially present only when the plant has died and become a corpse.

The third partner in the starch-forming process is oxygen, a study of which shows it to be cosmic life. Atmospheric and hydrospheric oxygen are its vehicles. Water, which is eighty-nine percent oxygen, brings this life-giving element to plants and thereby causes them to germinate and grow and come to earthly manifestation. Oxygen is in this sense the opposite pole of hydrogen. In *The Nature of Substance* I dubbed it 'life substance', and showed how the two elements are in the Goethean sense carriers of the polarity: being and appearance.

In spring, when the 'life substance' streams in life-giving moisture, when everything in nature grows new shoots and buds, the idea of the plant begins incarnating, reaching the zenith of material appearance at the height of summer. But when hydrogen takes over and causes the plant to wither up and disappear, leaving nothing but the seed behind, the being of the plant can be said to have withdrawn from visibility, only to use the seed as its means of reappearance in the following spring.

In carbohydrates, the rhythmic interchange between hydrogen and oxygen, between being and appearance, is fixed by carbon at the various stages. When carbon has reached a peak of activity, all rhythm ceases and the carbohydrates harden into the cellulose we see in the woody parts of plants. But when it is hydrogen's turn to culminate, the carbohydrates become formless, as in sugars and other more etherealized forms of plant substance.

Carbohydrates, then, are produced by the interplay of carbon, hydrogen and oxygen. But let it not be thought that we are referring to a combination of the three substances calculable in atomic weights. What we have in mind is rather an interweaving of cosmic essences capable of bringing forth a living entity: starch, in its various metamorphoses. Only with the destruction of this living entity is there a separation into the three substances, which are reduced to the corpses of a once-living organism.

In *The Nature of Substance* we suggested the symbolic representation of carbohydrates on page 45 as a way of picturing the interplay of dynamic chemical forces that produce these substances.

A predominance of one or the other essence produces the following substances:

> Predominance of cosmic form: cellulose
> Predominance of cosmic life: starches
> Predominance of cosmic fire: sugars

Protein is as characteristically the building material of the animal organism as carbohydrates are of plants. But at one point in its development the plant too forms protein. This is the moment when seed is developing. Seed forms in that part where plant and animal spheres overlap. At the blossoming stage, plants are surrounded by insects, caught up in a moving element which transfers pollen from one flower to the stigma of another. This process precipitates the protein of which seeds are made. It is not to be pictured as a direct transferring of animal substance to the seed on the part of insects. We are referring rather to the power of movement itself as it plays between universal space and the plant world that finds physical expression in vegetable protein. It is not a matter of any consequence that sometimes – as in the case of wind-pollinated plants – the fructifying animal's rôle is taken over by atmospheric motion. The nitrogen process is the force at work in either case.

In *The Nature of Substance* we renamed nitrogen and called it air-substance, or, on occasion, motion-substance. Nitrogen is the carrier of motion and of cosmic rhythm. In the Latin countries, nitrogen has a name still fragrant with a touch of cosmic reality, for there it is called 'azota', a word that comes from 'azure', meaning 'heaven's blue'. Plants, though tied to the immobile soil, become mobile in their seeds as a result of nitrogen activity. If seeds were not full of latent motion, the wind could not make them take to the air and go travelling. Nitrogen itself is a free agent in the air element. Eighty per cent of air is nitrogen, in a free (i.e., not chemically bound) condition. Indeed, where it is chemically bound, it becomes explosive. Explosives are actually motion in an imprisoned state.

The following diagram was included in *The Nature of Substance* as a way of picturing the chemical dynamics of protein:

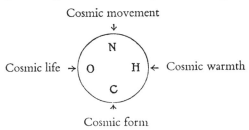

Cosmic movement

Cosmic life → O   H ← Cosmic warmth

N

C

Cosmic form

A wholly new element enters the picture with the production of animal protein; the gastrula. Its formation at a certain point in animal foetal developing represents a forward step in evolution beyond the plant stage. The gastrula folds back upon itself, thus creating an inside and an outside. The plant comes into being as the direct result of an interplay of cosmic forces. But animal development rests on a tendency to create a personal domain by shutting cosmic forces out of an area and developing inner organs in the resulting vacuum. All systems of organs are in this sense microcosms emancipated from the macrocosm, the organs within each such microcosm being dynamic centres that correspond to the creative forces of the enveloping macrocosm. The animal pre-empts and interiorizes part of the formative creativity of the universe to build up its own inner system of organs. While plant substance is produced by a direct radiating-in of cosmic forces and is bound up with external light, the animal's development of protein is the result of formative impulses proceeding from the cosmos which it has interiorized.

In the case of animal protein, it is therefore incorrect to speak as we did in the plant's case of cosmic form, cosmic fire forces, cosmic life and cosmic rhythm. Instead, we have to say organ form-forces, organ fire forces, organ life and organ rhythm. This would make our diagram of the chemical dynamics in animal protein the following:

$$
\begin{array}{c}
N \\
\uparrow \\
\text{Organ rhythm} \\
O \leftarrow \text{Organ life} \qquad \text{Organ fire} \rightarrow H \\
\text{Organ form} \\
\downarrow \\
C
\end{array}
$$

In speaking of the animal organism as an inverted cosmos and of the organs as fountainheads of these inner-cosmic forces, we have to think of the latter as reflected star forces. In this connection we recall that the priests of olden times actually read the will of the gods from the organs of sacrificial animals, while in other lands and cultures priests found divine guidance in the movement of the stars.

A further such new element is found in the case of human nature. In the animal kingdom, the generic principle is all-important, ordering the various creatures into species, types and classes. It is proper to call this ordering principle the group soul. The ancients attributed such influences to the constellations. In man's case, the sun has the dominant rôle as the representative and unifier of all the other cosmic elements. It is the directing principle that introduces the harmonious order called reason or intelligence into both the human form and human mind. Only superficially is the difference between man and animal seen as a question of degree and gradual differentiation, of nervous endowment and brain dimension. We must counter this with the statement of an entirely new basic principle to be found in man. The human mind is not to be explained by amounts of brain and nerve substance alone, but by the fact that man's whole shape and organism are such as to make them suitable carriers of the thinking spirit. Animals act instinctively as the result of their enchainment and limitation to a certain body-form. Man acts out of free, individual conviction, a fact made possible by his possession of a truly resolved and universal form. The single bee has no intelligence: it is the colony as a whole that possesses wisdom by virtue of its inclusion within a group-soul. Man alone is a species unto himself and of solar rank.

The plant is the carrier of the life principle, the animal of the psyche, man of the spirit.

What, we may ask, are the material tools at the disposal of the human spirit?

Here again, superficial observers point out the similarity between animal and human protein and use it to support their view that man is just a higher animal. But human protein is as different from animal protein as the latter is from vegetable protein.

We have to realize clearly that though animals embody the soul principle, they retain a plant aspect as well, due to the fact that they are living creatures. And we do indeed find substances connected with the more vegetative functions of the animal organism that remind us of plant matter.

As a living creature, man too has the plant principle built into his vegetative functions. Both in the human blood and liver there are carbohydrates.

But man is endowed with a soul as well as with life, and thus also shares the animal principle. The material support of his soul nature is human protein. But exclusively human substance is again characterized by a new element; thus we see iron making its appearance as an essential factor in the human make-up. A study of iron convinces one that this is a highly significant substance. It is a peculiar property of iron forces that they radiate in from peripheral space, that they bring elements distributed throughout the macrocosm to a microcosmic focussing point. In *The Nature of Substance* we came to know iron as the carrier of personality forces. An iron deficiency as it were takes the ground out from under a person, as is plainly apparent in certain pathological conditions. Iron has the function of making blood out of protein. Blood is indeed 'a very special fluid', as is said in *Faust*, being the substance that carries body, soul and spirit. It is the substance that governs the individual rhythms of each human organism.

Higher mammals also have iron in their blood. But here the story is similar to that of vegetable protein, which comes into being where plant and animal spheres overlap. The iron present in the red blood of higher mammals comes from an overlapping of the animal and human spheres. This is not to say that domestic animals are the only ones with iron in their blood, for wild animals also have it. We saw that actual insects are not an absolute essential of the pollenizing process, that protein can be produced in seeds by the cosmic animal-forming process as this lives in atmospheric motion. The process that forms human beings radiates similarly into the iron in the blood of higher animals.

Human blood is, however, very different indeed from animal blood. This is true not only of its composition, but above all of its nature, as may be seen in the shape of the blood corpuscules and many another physiological phenomenon. Only human blood has a constant temperature, for example, and this 98·4 degrees warmth is the basis of human personality. At the point where the breathing rhythm impinges on the blood, a cosmic pattern leaves its imprint. The human breathing rhythm is linked up with the sun rhythm of the so-called Platonic year. Just as it takes the sun 25,920 years to complete its round of the zodiac, human beings breathe 25,920 times in the course of twenty-four hours. One human breath is thus like a sun-year. There are four pulse-beats to every normal human breath. Man is the only creature whose blood moves in harmony with the sun rhythm.

Blood, then, courses through man's organism subject to universal laws and has its central organ in the heart, which may be called the central organ of man's personality, the sun of each human microcosm. In the world outside us, it is the sun's warmth that makes plants grow and blossom and pour out colour and fragrance till they fade away. In the inner world these same cosmic-fire qualities can be recognized in the heart with its warmth of feeling. The heart is the seat of those upward-flaming fire forces that shape human individuality, enable man to feel enthusiasm, and give the world of the spirit a human dwelling place.

All this shows that blood contains a protein element related to hydrogen.

The lungs envelop the heart. Cosmic formative forces are taken up by them with every indrawn breath. It is characteristic of the lungs that carbon, not oxygen or nitrogen, should be their native element. And this carbon is by no means completely exhaled as carbon dioxide, but is used as the shaping earth element, in a process that ends in bone formation. This is a fact not too well known today, and its consequences go unappreciated. Carbon is earth substance, and hence the material out of which the lungs' activity fashions the image of each personality in his bony framework. It is also the formative force that, freed from its shaping function in the maturing organism, moulds thought and directs the activity of our consciousness. We have said of carbon that it embodies the cosmic formative forces of the universal thought-sphere. In man's case, carbon is the carrier of form, both for his thinking spirit and his individually shaped body.

The liver is the organ that connects human substance with the life element. Forces proceeding from the liver impregnate human protein with vitality. Rudolf Steiner called the liver the 'chemicator' of the human organism, meaning that all liver functions take place, as chemical reactions do, in the fluid element. The preparation of the various bodily fluids goes on in a continual interchange of taking up and secreting, of an internal chemicalizing. Chyle and lymph are both under the liver's jurisdiction, and the portal-vein blood that is transformed in the liver flows from this organ directly to the heart.

According to Rudolf Steiner, the kidneys are suction organs. They join forces with the bladder to draw air from the whole organism. The liquefied urea and water excreted are really air. This is difficult to grasp unless one regains a living understanding of the old Aristotelian elements. These are not elements in the sense of modern chemistry and physics, but factors that include the inner being along with the outer. In this case it is the being of airy or gaseous nature. We are concerned here with presenting the total complex of the life and functioning of the organs from one angle only. The author is quite familiar with the problem of having to live a long time with Rudolf Steiner's indications on life processes before really grasping them. His concepts have an entirely different character, and there are not always new terms to convey them adequately. From this point of view, the kidneys are the primary means of taking breath, the lungs serving only as an aid to the kidneys in completing the process. The kidneys may accordingly be looked upon as organs of motion: the motion of air through the human organism. On a higher level, this function takes the form of soul movement, feeling and mental activity. The nervous system that is the carrier of these higher functions is closely linked up with and part of the kidney system's total functioning.

These four organizing systems, then, radiate the forces that build truly human substance. As in the case of the plant, which produces carbohydrates in the form of starches, sugar, and cellulose according as cosmic life, cosmic fire, and cosmic formative forces take the dominant rôle, human substance is built into blood, nerves, bone or lymph according as the fire of the heart, or the kidney (functioning as the organ of the air-process), the lung as bearer of formative forces, or the liver (as the organ that stimulates a living chemical process) is most active.

These organs are stimulated to activity from two different angles. The first is physical food. The second is the spiritual nutriment we described as deriving from thought and sense perception.

CHAPTER SIX

Man as a Threefold Being

In ancient times it was taken as a matter of course that man was a being of inter-related body, soul and spirit. 'Mens sana in corpore sano' – a healthy mind in a healthy body – was the Romans' way of putting it, and they were right. But that is only one aspect. Nowadays we ought to complement it with 'and a healthy *body* as a result of a healthy *spirit*'.

This probably sounds absurd to modern ears. But let us explore the reasons for its validity.

Both the above theses can really be understood only by a painstaking study of man from a spiritual-scientific angle. Many people find this difficult because they have not yet realized that thinking is itself a process subject to evolutionary change. The nineteenth century was the first to grasp the idea of evolution, through Haeckel. But it was grasped only by the natural sciences and affected those aspects of man comprehensible to such sciences as genetics and embryology. That thinking itself is subject to continuing change and evolution is a fact that Rudolf Steiner was the first to point out (in his book *The Philosophy of Spiritual Activity*). We in the twentieth century are on the very verge of a new development of thinking. The birthpangs are everywhere apparent.

We have made use of our thoughts to develop techniques which aim to build a civilization based on comfort. Those who notice how narrow and egotistical this self-serving use of thought is may also find, as they observe themselves, that their thinking has become shadowy and abstract; it can no longer lay hold on the reality of the cosmos. Such individuals may begin to wonder what would happen if they served thinking instead of making it serve them. What would be the result of making oneself a perceptive organ for the power of thought, of concentrating one's whole being in the act of listening? One who practices this art will find himself able, with this selfless new thinking, to enter the realm of living metamorphosis, where thoughts grow and become expressions of the creative thinking of the cosmos. He comes into touch with objective reality, with essential being.

Mankind has advanced from its early state of visionary picture consciousness to one capable of imageless, abstract, conceptual thinking. But as the spiritual world was lost from view, thought became ever less able to grasp reality. The earth became man's conquest, but only in the superficial sense dictated by physically oriented causal thinking. The time has now come to broaden thinking and so rise to a new 'view' of reality.

New capacities are always first demonstrated by a few fore-runners, and only gradually become the possession of the race. Goethe's 'anschauende Urteilskraft' – seeing the thing meant in the thing seen – was the start, the dawning, of the new thinking that can carry the thinker to the core of reality: the beings who create it. His ideas were living reality in this sense, and he spoke of actually 'seeing' them when he described his primal plant. Rudolf Steiner evolved from this new way of attaining know-ledge a perfect tool and used it as the method for his Anthropo-sophy. This gave rise to a new science of man capable of illumi-nating every realm of life and life's connection with what is of the soul and spirit.

Orthodox medicine is beginning to grant that man is more than a mere mechanism that can be summed up as a complex of physical and chemical processes and repaired accordingly. But that soul and spirit are as real as the body is still not admitted; they are usually looked upon as the body's emanations. Psychology is now a century old. But its history, ranging from Fechner, via Helmholtz, Wundt, Freud and Watson to modern 'faculty psychology' shows only too plainly that the poor evolving soul is given only the semblance of a trial before being condemned to death.

But that body, soul and spirit are geared to interact harmoni-ously as one single organism, with health or illness the result, is a fact that goes almost totally unrecognized. The material of which the human body is composed is not only alive, but also permeated with soul and spirit. Their inter-relationship can be made clear by a study of the blood and nerves.

In *Faust* we are told that 'Blood is a very special fluid'. The human being can work directly in and through it. Soul and spirit are indissolubly bound up with the blood and live in it. This

46

means that those human impulses that spring from man's warm-bloodedness are spontaneous. The will-component of the soul has its physical base in blood. At the present time we have no consciousness whatsoever of how the will functions. In those depths where moral substance is engendered we are sound asleep. Will impulses rise up, and only when they are there before us do we know of their existence and have a chance to subject them to a conscious scrutiny.

Perception and judgment are, however, activities based, not on blood-warmth, but on the coolness native to our nerves. Nerves too are a special form of matter, in that soul and spirit have withdrawn from them. Indeed, the nerves cannot even hold onto life, and are always on the verge of dying. Everyone knows that nerves have very slight regenerative power. Flesh wounds heal quickly, whereas brain injuries always have serious and irreparable consequences and are often fatal. There is a deep secret behind this fact: consciousness is bought at the expense of life. Put in Biblical terms: eating of the Tree of Knowledge meant being denied access to the Tree of Life in the garden of Paradise.

Knowledge always implies a 'solution', a dissolving-out of truth from a nexus of data. If the spirit seeking knowledge were to remain as completely involved with data as the will is with the blood, consciousness could never develop. But the free spirit can mirror itself objectively in the nerves. Members of family groups can only come to an objective judgment of some event that stirs up the whole clan if they have freed themselves from subjection to the tribal spirit.

An illustration drawn from the more readily understandable inorganic realm may give us a better grasp of this. In *The Nature of Substance* I described iron as a chemically active substance that participates most energetically in chemical reactions, whereas platinum, just the opposite, is totally inactive. Platinum is the last of a series of substances: iron, cobalt, nickel, chromium, manganese, and so on, which exhibit decreasing chemical activity. Platinum is completely dead in this respect. But they all have a powerful chemical effect on their surroundings. Their mere presence sets off chemical reactions, even though they are not themselves materially involved. Chemists call these substances catalysts. In their case, the chemical action is not attached to the substance in question, but is a free chemical force that surrounds the dead or dying substance, like an aura or a potentiality. Platinum paid for its capacity to be a free chemical agent with material death.

Nerves and blood have their seat in opposite poles of the organism: the nerves in the sense-system, the blood in the limbs

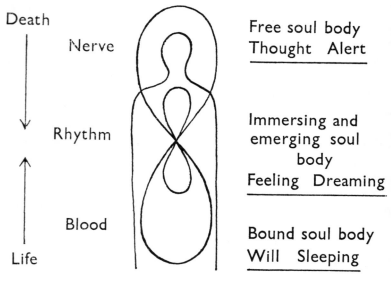

Fig. 7
The relationship between body, soul and spirit and the
physiological basis of thought, feeling and will.

and metabolism. The head is actually that part of the body most subject to death's hardening forces, whereas the life-giving metabolism carries on its work of bodily regeneration without any conscious effort on our part.

Between the nerve and metabolic poles lies the realm of the human rhythmic system, where bodily life and man's soul and spiritual principles alternately come together and separate. This breath of life, which continues on into the pulsing of the blood, wrests itself free from the metabolism's sleeping depths, but cannot quite achieve the head's wide-awake state of consciousness.

Here we find the bodily seat of the soul, the feeling principle. Joy and sorrow have an immediate effect on the pulse and the breathing rhythm. We may describe feeling-consciousness as comparable to dreaming; it is a state midway between waking thought and sleeping will.

This picture of man's entelechy is essential to an adequate hygiene based on reality. For any disturbance of the inter-relationship between body, soul and spirit brings about illness.

Man's soul is already being recognized as the real cause of ill health. Physicians are becoming increasingly interested in the psychic beginning-stages of disease, before organic disturbances have become evident.

The human organism may be compared to a scale, with the rhythmic system holding the balance between the nerve and blood poles. Sclerotic and inflammatory illnesses are caused by the hardening nerve processes impinging on the metabolism or the fire processes of the blood intruding into the nerve realm.

So we find a psychic or spiritual correlate for every bodily malaise, and the truth of our statement that 'a healthy spirit makes for a healthy body' becomes evident. A better way of putting it would be: 'a healthy body is the result of a healthy connection of body and spirit'.

This body is put at the disposal of the incarnating spirit at conception. During the foetal period, childhood and youth, the soul and spirit have to remodel it into an instrument suited to their use. This is not always a simple matter. It is difficult for the higher principles to penetrate the bodily forms they find themselves confronted with. Developmental problems and illnesses are the outcome. The so-called diseases of childhood, measles, scarlet fever, diphtheria and so on, should be looked upon as the coming to grips of an individual spirit with an inherited body. If there are really serious obstacles to be dealt with – deformations of the organs due to congenital or accidental causes – the individuality cannot incarnate properly. A deformed body makes for a deranged soul-world, exactly as a crooked mirror gives a distorted reflection. This is the background of so-called psychic illness. 'Mens sana in corpore sano' attains real meaning only in the context of a fuller modern view of man.

We see from the above what a tremendously important rôle education plays, along with a spiritual-scientific nutritional hygiene, in preparing the young to take their place in life as whole human beings.

The fact that man is made up of body, soul and spirit and that these work together in his organism accounts for his having three systems in his bodily organization: the metabolism, breath and blood circulation, and the nerve-sense apparatus. We refer here, of course, to the *living* body. We have already studied life phenomena in plants, and seen how they are built up by the cosmos, given life and shape, and become physically manifest. But the essential being that is the reality behind each such appearance is an aggregate of forces that builds itself an archetypal form out of streaming cosmic elements, densifies it into matter, brings it into order and motion, and makes of it a living organism. But we learned too that man has such an aggregate of forces which he has built into his system of internal organs; what plants receive in the way of formative forces direct from sun and moon and stars comes in man's case from within himself. This aggregate of shaping energies, which maintains the physical organism and is the tool whereby the individual human spirit sculpts that organism into a living image of itself, can be called, appropriately, 'life body'.

A complete listing of the various parts of the human entelechy has to differentiate between the physical and life bodies. What has been said above probably makes it obvious that the connection between the two is especially strong in the blood, while in the nerves life has been partially released along with soul and spirit.

One of Rudolf Steiner's most helpful discoveries was finding the connection between the four parts of man and the four elements of the human body. Aristotle gave a comprehensive exposition of the four elements as reflections of earthly states and energies. We can go further and make a study of the way the various members of man's being express themselves and function in the bones, the blood, the breath, and the warmth-organism.

The physical body is more, of course, than just the bony framework. It includes physically measurable warmth, the air in the body, fluids, muscles and organs, as well as the denser parts.

However, the skeleton is the purest expression of the physical laws obtaining in the body; formative forces have made it an image of the personality that inhabits it.

The life body works in a way directly counter to the physical. It makes the heavy light, dissolves what has hardened, brings fixed form into flowing motion, re-enlivens the dying. In the plant kingdom, life-giving water is the matrix out of which cosmic forces bring pure being into manifestation. Chemical energies of sound, of tone, are the cosmic alchemists that bring forth, metamorphose and again erase the marvels of material creation. And this life body is active chiefly in the body fluids: blood, lymph and tissue-fluids. It is the key to the mysteries of digestion and the metabolism.

Motion is the soul's native element. Breathing and blood circulation enable it to travel throughout the organism. Air, the carrier of soul forces in the blood, is made up of oxygen and carbonic acid, which flow to and from the heart in rhythmic alternation. What on the bodily level is motion becomes feeling, illumination, on the level of the soul.

The ego, bearer of man's spirit, lives in the warmth element. Warmth is the spirit's bodily vehicle. The will and the deeds in which we make our personal mark on life spring from the blood's fire. And where the ego frees itself from a connection with the body, as in the case of the nerves, the fire of enthusiasm is its characteristic element.

Earth	Formative forces	Physical body
Water	Chemism, Musical forces }	Life body
Air	Light	Soul
Fire		Ego

CHAPTER SEVEN

Protein as a Food

The formation of human protein is an act of the inner man whom we studied in preceding chapters. The protein that turns up in our blood and organs is by no means the same substance that we once consumed. Our bodies are built up by the most subtle and mysterious functions comparable in kind to the sublime processes that link sun, moon, stars and earth.

But a most essential stimulus is given to the process of human protein building by earthly protein foods.

Protein is, indeed, the primal food. It has to be available from the very start of life. It is present in the germ-cell, and the maternal organism builds up a protein embryo before soul and spirit have made it their abode. The infant's first food is its mother's milk: again, protein from her organism. Protein was the original food of all mankind when, in that earliest period of its history, it was organized to absorb the surrounding protein atmosphere. Protein is still absolutely essential in maintaining the physical body. It is a sort of sculptor, providing the material best suited for building up man's body.

As we have seen, protein is also the most easily digestible of foods. This makes it extremely important to infants, young children and convalescents. Significant though this function of stimulating the building-up of the body is, however, protein can lead healthy adults very much astray.

What do we mean by this?

Digestion is a faculty of each individual's most personal being. This was discussed in detail in the chapter on the history of nutrition. We showed there how the ego is the force responsible for sublimating the nutritive stream through the intestinal wall and into the blood. Since protein is an already highly organized substance – and this is especially true of protein from animal and human sources, as in milk – the work of assimilation left for the ego is not arduous.

But what if these digestive forces never have to make any greater effort? What happens to a person who has a faculty but makes no use of it? The capacity and the energy degenerate. They become like a healthy limb always kept in a splint or a plaster cast, they lose their mobility.

In the present phase of human evolution, man is beginning to be a creator in his own right. One expression of this fact as it affects nutrition is the ego's ability to digest plant matter and even minerals. But we lose capacities that are not constantly exercised.

Too much protein in the diet causes the body functions to grow slack, and in time even makes for mental and spiritual slackness. Deposits, stones, gout and sclerosis are consequences of taking it easy in this sense. Psychic concomitants are alternating dullness and irritability, which can become extremely severe.

The opposite pole, too little protein, threatens the body-soul balance by failing to provide the ego with a sufficiently sturdy bodily foundation. Cases of this sort tend to tuberculosis. The lungs play a remarkable part in this, for they are the organs that make us citizens of the earth. It is their function, in processing oxygen, to take those substances that have passed through the intestinal wall and become non-material and materialize them again into living human protein. The power to do this is disturbed in the tubercular. Protein in the diet stimulates this function.

Proper protein nutrition depends to a great extent on the form in which we use it and the kingdoms of nature from which it comes.

There is no doubt that the healthiest protein is that taken from the vegetable kingdom – whole rye bread, for example. But other plant products, seeds and nuts especially, offer us a wide choice of quite adequate proteins. Legumes such as beans, peas and lentils, are richer in protein than any other kind of plant, but they contain it in a form that made Pythagoras forbid his disciples to eat them. The dulling of consciousness that follows the partaking of a bean dish is due to the fact that legumes weigh down the metabolism as animal proteins do. This point will be more fully discussed in a later chapter.

Animal proteins like milk, eggs and meat are still the main source of this food element.

Milk is the substance most adapted to the human organism and is therefore the most suitable and easily digested food for infants and young children. It should be noted that pasteurizing and cooking denature fresh raw milk and make it harder to digest. Even seemingly harmless handling affects the quality of milk. Professor Malyoth-München produced evidence showing that a few hours' storage in an icebox brought about a denaturing that changed the healthy Bifidus-stools of infants fed on mother's milk into unhealthy ones with signs of fermentation and other intestinal disturbances.

Milk and milk products remain important foods for later life as well. Milk produces vital forces that give the power of healing to a person whose chief nourishment it is. Physicians connected with the mysteries of olden times took milk as a means of enhancing this power. Milk helps a person come down to earth rightly and to develop a feeling for the oneness of the human race. An old custom illustrates this. It was permissible, in some Germanic tribes, for fathers to expose and thus put to death a new-born baby up to the moment when it drank the first drop of milk. Taking milk signified its reception into the tribal community, and its exposure after this event was considered murder. Milk, then, welcomes the heavenly being of the child to earth and makes it an earth-citizen without interfering with its belonging as well to the whole solar system, according to Rudolf Steiner.

Meat, quite the opposite, enchains one to earth. But why is this?

Milk is the product of a damming of reproductive forces, and is an undifferentiated, basic substance, just bordering on the animal. The production of milk depends far more on the animal's vital forces than on its drives and instincts. We said in an earlier chapter that animal protein was the most easily digested food because it is a substance lifted above the plant stage and to such a high level of organization by the digestive work animals have done on it as to require very little further digestive effort on the part of the human consumer.

But we must take the following facts into consideration. Plants lift lifeless minerals to their own life-level. When they eat plants, human beings have to take up the work of reorganization at the point where the plant left off and carry it to a point two stages higher, through the animal to the human level. Though animals, too, reorganize the plants they eat, they do so in a way very different from the human. Animal protein thus represents a real burden on the human body. The more developed and creative the person is, the more oppressive does this load seem. Meat weighs one down with earthly heaviness, and stirs up instinctive will forces which express themselves in passion and emotion. It is thus a food that chains one to the earth. As Rudolf Steiner put it, it has the effect of making us feel quite satisfied to lose heaven if we gain the earth thereby.

CHAPTER EIGHT

Fats as Foods

What is the effect of fat in the diet? Man has the capacity to produce his own fats. But he still needs to have this process stimulated by fat which he consumes in foods. Nutritional scientists reckon in calories the amounts needed to maintain life while the body is at rest and not exerting itself. It should be perfectly evident that this is pure abstraction. The food ration officially set for the peoples of conquered Central Europe in the years following World War II and as late as 1948 did not always measure up to what was deemed essential to maintain life – and this in a nation that was not just lying abed resting, but spent some of the time at strenuous labour. Human beings simply cannot be thought of as combustion engines to be kept going with a certain amount of fuel, the energy output of which can be reckoned in advance: they are, rather, the scene of an interchange between cosmic and earthly forces. All projecting of non-human outer laws of nature into man the microcosm is as wrong as it is to project laws that apply only to earthly space and time out into the universe.

We can therefore say that the number of calories thought essential to an adequate diet is not necessarily required. What is actually needed is the stimulation of the vital processes which fat in the diet provides.

Fat is not a body-building material in the sense we have learned that protein is; its rôle is to supply a foundation for the life processes taking place in the various organs. Fat is deposited in the organism and then used as a source of warmth. All the functions of the human organs require embedding in a constant warmth, and fat plays an important part in producing it. A fat deficiency tends to make the organ functions torpid, with the result that the physical body becomes inelastic and brittle and the life body insufficiently active.

The important thing here is to find the right balance between fat-intake and waking activity. This balance is always highly individual, for a person's relation to fat is a faithful mirror of the way his ego is active in the sphere of life.

The purely vegetative functions that build the body are, then, dependent upon fat to do their work. Too great a fat intake depresses the psychic-spiritual functions that are linked to break-down processes in the body, and the life-sense takes on a phleg-matic colouring. It can be especially harmful to combine a diet high in fats with a great deal of sleep, for this encourages body-building at the expense of soul and spiritual activity and makes the fat imbalance permanent. Fat is then deposited all over the body, like so much ballast.

Just as the lungs play the most important rôle in the body's use of protein, the liver is the organ most involved in taking care of fats. First it produces the gall that combines with the intestinal trypsin and breaks the fat down. Then, it is the organ that re-enlivens human substance after it has had all the life taken out of it in the intestines. The liver reacts at once to a wrong fat diet, while a sick liver cannot take care of fat at all.

The question of source is as important with fats as we found it to be in the case of proteins. Unhealthy deposits of unenlivened fat are due to the type of fat consumed. Vegetable oils come directly from the cosmos. In summer, plants stream out through their blossoms into universal space, and the universe responds with the oil that appears in the ripening seed. Animal fats are, however, the product of the animal's own organism and bear the imprint of its special nature. But these fats do not have such strong animalistic effects on the human consumer as does protein.

It is really amazing how different the various fats are in structure and appearance. A table of comparative density, measured by the temperature at which they melt (p. 58), is most revealing.

Human fat tests between goose fat and fish liver oil. This shows that man occupies a certain middle position, that his vital processes are more plantlike than animal.

Custom and prevailing fashion created a demand for fats with a butter consistency, manufacturers sought eagerly for ways to harden vegetable oils and came up with margarine. Oils of tropical plants such as palms and coconuts (the dried meat is sold as 'copra') are its chief ingredients, though it contains some fish oils as well.

Chemists speak of fats being 'saturated', oils 'unsaturated'. This

	Melting point
Beef tallow	48°C.
Sheep tallow	45°C.
Butter fat	37°C.
Pork fat	35°C.
Rabbit fat	28°C.
Goose fat	25°C.
Fish liver oil	0°C.
Peanut oil	− 3°C.
Rapeseed oil	− 5°C.
Olive oil	− 10°C.
Beechnut oil	− 15°C.
Almond oil	− 15°C.
Walnut oil	− 18°C.
Poppyseed oil	− 18°C.
Hazelnut oil	− 20°C.
Flaxseed oil	− 25°C.

is pictured in structural chemistry's symbology by single links in the saturated, double links in the unsaturated carbon chain. The hardening process used in big factories consists in heating the oils under pressure with hydrogen and finely ground nickel as catalysts, causing them to become saturated.

Fats so hardened are of course highly denatured, and they are made more so by the addition of a synthetic yellow dye and butter flavouring.

So-called synthetic fats made of mineral oils are unsuitable as human foods. Germany has a number of factories engaged in producing these for use in soaps. We should not let ourselves think that such synthetic fats are harmless to the human body. As they are not absorbed and used, they could in time coat and paralyze the living tissue of the mucous membranes lining the intestines.

CHAPTER NINE

Carbohydrates as Foods

Plants are composed essentially of carbohydrates. This is a being that extends out to the stars and is built up with the sun's assistance from far reaches of the universe as a carrier of life.

In comparison man is a carrier of soul and spirit. He builds his body with his own vital processes. But soul and spirit have to break down the body to achieve consciousness. The sun outside us creates green plants. The sun inside causes partial death as the price of reversing the plant process and lifting man to his human level. Man is creation's further step beyond the plant stage, in that soul and spirit destroy what is plant-like in him in order to incorporate the nervous system. Life is thus raised to the level of consciousness. The light of which external plants are built works within man, Rudolf Steiner tells us, on the renewal of his nervous system.

Animal foods already contain developed animal soul forces, which human consumers have to overcome. Animals have of course done some preliminary work of reorganization, but a human being cannot just take animal foods and build entirely according to his own individual intentions, from the bottom up. As we have shown, such foods have a quite specific effect on the nervous system and thus too on the consumer's soul life.

Plant foods, on the other hand, leave the nervous system entirely undisturbed. This makes it possible for the consumer to limit effects on his nerves to those stimuli which have their origin in his own being. We are indebted to the plants we eat for our ability to rise to the larger view of things that lifts us above prejudice and passion.

Meat fosters a personally coloured outlook, while plant foods help us achieve a broad perspective. Both types of attitudes are handed down in the hereditary stream from generation to generation, and the influence of a long history of meat eating by our forefathers is often so strong that it cannot be thrown off in the course of a lifetime. In such cases, inherited matter simply goes its own way. Rudolf Steiner tells us that this can be the source of nervous afflictions, epilepsy and hysteria.

Vegetarianism has some justification in the light of these facts. However, it also has certain limitations and dangers too, in the perspective of an individual's total dietary needs. In our discussion of fats and proteins we called attention to the crippling effect of having capacities but failing to use them. In the case of a vegetable diet we must point out the opposite danger of the incapacity some people have to digest vegetables.

As we have said, digestion is a function of the ego. It consists in converting foods to an immaterial, spiritualized condition in which they can serve as stimulants for further inner processes. If this function is disturbed by an individual's incapacity fully to spiritualize the foods he eats, they cannot be assimilated and must be excreted as foreign matter. Improperly digested foods result in flatulence. This comes from an organism's inability to transform and reorganize the air it absorbs, in turn depressing the digestive function. The kidneys play a most important part in this, for they depend on the 'inner light' derived from the proper digestion of carbohydrates to build up the nervous system and maintain its functions. It will be remembered from an earlier chapter that the kidneys govern the body's air-organism. They, with the bladder, draw the airy element of the whole organism toward them. They are thus the prime cause of our in-breathing.

An incapacity to digest carbohydrates properly can lead to serious disturbances of a person's whole constitution. The most striking example is diabetes. Here we find the organism able to digest carbohydrates only to the point of converting them to sugars, but unable to 'sublimate' them through the intestinal wall. As a result they pass into the blood unchanged, are foreign matter there, and must be excreted.

Right as vegetarian practice is, fanaticism is all wrong. Vegetarianism can be advanced only by insight into its importance in man's wholesome bodily and spiritual development – insight based on a really modern, spiritual grasp of man and nature.

Everyone has to discover for himself what he can expect of his digestive powers. It is not right to judge the strength of a person's ego by his ability or inability to live on vegetables. Those who cannot are not necessarily weaklings; it may be that the ego simply fails to take a healthy interest in digestion. In a later discussion of spices we will go into this problem more thoroughly.

To suggest, as has been done here, that carbohydrates are responsible for building and maintaining the nervous system with the help of man's air and light organism is a new departure. So-called scientific findings of more recent date have inclined us all to the view that the human organism is purely material. Laws of nature are substituted for spiritual fact showing how easily we fall into the unconscious habit of conceiving of man as a physical body made up of chemical substances interacting with each other. We have pursued matter as far as its chemical elements and we now seek to show, as best we can, how matter works and how, chemically, it behaves in man, the great retort. But even a plant's vital processes give a new turn and context to forces and substances, so that they are made to work quite differently than was the case before this involvement. Man, as a being of soul and spirit, transforms and redirects the substances absorbed by him in ways of which we have as yet only dim premonitions.

It is often considered an advance in scientific thinking to regard man as a huge retort where chemical processes go on. Rudolf Steiner says, however, that 'the time will come when the (spiritual) facts about light and the soul of man just presented will be perceptible to researchers in their laboratories. Chemical experiments will demonstrate plainly how the most sublime works in the most commonplace.'

In *The Nature of Substance* I devoted a chapter to discussing the three carbohydrate categories: starch, sugar and cellulose. The virgin substance starch is produced by light, air and water through the process called assimilation. What can be described as a materialization of the drama of colour witnessed in rainbows is primal creation repeating itself all over again. And the starch it produces appears in all sorts and degrees of different forms and qualities in plants that grow in the various regions of the earth. The formative elements that give landscapes, plants and grains of starch the shapes they have are characterized by the same dangers and biasses found in East and West: losing oneself to the point of formlessness in the East, enchainment to matter in the West.

The starch kernels of wheat, rye and barley harmonize the polarities found in rice and potato starch, both as to shape and size. European grain starch kernels all have forms that remind one of tiny suns with concentric layers grouped around their centres. European cereals are indeed the right diet for Europeans. We will have more to say on the subject of potatoes in a later chapter.

Cellulose – the hardest, densest form of carbohydrate – is the structural material of plants. We find it in vegetables as well as in the husks of grain, and eat it in all whole-grain foods. It is an element wrongly thought of as worthless as a food. To be sure, it is given some recognition as a 'bulk' provider, but this fails to do justice to its real importance. Skeletal and outer parts of fruits and vegetables are said to be indigestible, but are nevertheless tolerated because they are thought to stimulate the intestinal function and thus aid elimination.

Not only is elimination far more than just the removal of waste products, as we pointed out above, but 'bulk foods' are actually nutrients. This will be discussed at length in a later chapter on salt and vitamins. In the meantime let it be noted that the ego is strengthened by the challenge these dense structural elements present.

Plants refine their substance into sugar in their blossom. Bees gather honey in the nectaries there, and we enjoy sugar in the levulose of sweet-tasting fruits. But plants like sugar cane and sugar beet store sugar in their stems or roots. A chapter of *The Nature of Substance* was devoted to a thorough discussion of their quality and nutritive value. We will content ourselves here with a brief recapitulation.

Honey is mentioned in the most ancient documents. It was the primeval form of sugar.

The conquests of Alexander brought a new development with them. When Alexander led his armies through Persia to India, the Greeks came upon 'a reed that brings forth honey unaided by bees'. This was the sugar cane already then under cultivation in India. Its culture spread through Persia to Egypt and soon became known to the whole civilized world of the period. It was the Arabs who discovered how to crystallize its sap and carried on a highly developed sugar business. The boiled sap was poured into cones made of palm leaves, thus creating the original sugar-loaves.

Charlemagne did much to further the Oriental spice trade, and this included sugar. Then the crusades helped to spread the European use of sugar. Columbus took sugar cane to America, and thus gave rise to the sugar plantations that now occupy eighty percent of the arable land of Cuba.

Sugar remained a luxury, however, through the greater part of the Middle Ages. It was only in comparatively recent times that Frederick the Great, Maria Theresa and Joseph the Second, those 'enlightened despots', decreed that sugar was to be regarded as a food, whereupon they eased its importation by lowering duties and taxes on it. The sugar industry took a tremendous spurt, as the imported raw brown sugar had to be refined and crystallized.

'Then', as an old account tells, 'all this progress was halted by the invention of an artificial substitute'. About 1800, the German scientist F. A. Achard discovered that sugar beets contained exploitable amounts of sugar. It took another twenty years to breed beets with enough sugar in them to warrant their production on a commercial scale. But things would never have developed as they did, in spite of all the ingenuity spent on the problem by German scientists and engineers, had the world situation not forced them.

Napoleon had set up his blockade of the Continent, effectively stopping the import of raw sugar into Europe. The efforts being made to produce an equally satisfactory sugar from the sugar beet were redoubled. Napoleon himself took a lively interest in the progress of the industry, so that 1811 saw a number of factories already in production. The young industry kept going after the fall of Napoleon for the simple reason that it was technically far superior to that in cane sugar. Even today it would be hard to find any other branch of industry that could match the thoroughness and logic with which every phase of its production has been thought out.

These historical considerations help to give us a picture of the nutritive qualities of the various kinds of sugar. The passage of time has meant a gradual descent from the blossom to the stem, then to the root:

Blossom	Honey	Time of the Patriarchs
Stem	Cane sugar	Alexander the Great
Root	Beet sugar	Napoleon

From the standpoint of shape, material and function, the blossom, stem and root are three clearly distinguished portions of the plant. They belong together as three parts of an organism. But each of the parts is designed to perform one distinct function. The blossom element links plants with the world that arches over them, the root element with earth. In stem and leaves, heaven and earth come together in a single harmony of interaction.

Honey is the product of cosmic influences in the plant. And the life lived in the times of the patriarchs was equally permeated by impulses that came directly from the spiritual world into men's wills. There was as yet no such thing as personal will and personal concepts. Individuality was still undeveloped.

Central Europe was undergoing its consolidation in the cane sugar period. Cities were being built up; efforts were being made to introduce some social order and sense of belonging into the conglomerate of peoples, and everyday life was deeply permeated by religion. All this indicates that feeling was then the guiding principle.

Then came our time, a period when thinking seems as deeply immersed in things of earth as the sugar beet is deeply rooted in the soil. Present-day thought is in this sense rootlike. In our time, the world's affairs are governed by intellect and reason except where the dawning of a new age already makes itself felt in a premonitory glow.

Honey is harvested without any resort to technology worth mentioning. In the Middle Ages, with its palm-leaf moulds, cane sugar production too was still very close to nature. But beet sugar production rests upon the most complex technological devices.

Thus we see a change in the state of human consciousness going hand in hand with changes in human eating habits. The example sugar presents is but one of many, and a study of these dietary matters always confirms the same principle.

Sugars, however, occupy a place of special interest in that honey, cane and beet sugar, representatives of the threefold plant, have taken turns as man's companions in his journey through time.

The threefold plant is not only to be found, as we have described, in human history: it is built into each individual human organism. A study of morphological and physiological aspects of the body shows that the formative forces active in the roots of plants build man's nerve and sense organism, while those forces active in the blossom are the same that power man's will and metabolism. In the central zone between head and limbs that houses the rhythmical functions of breathing and circulation and is the seat of human feeling, we find the same forces that work in the stems and foliage of plants.

One of Rudolf Steiner's most impressive discoveries was that of the relationship of thinking, will and feeling to the threefold structure of the body as the physiological basis of man's soul life. According to this, thinking rests upon the nerve and sense organism, feeling on the rhythmic system, will on the limbs and metabolism. The confusion that reigns in modern physiology comes from thinking of the soul as an emanation of the nervous system. The whole man is needed to support the life of soul and spirit. We 'grasp' in thought and feel out with our breathing the things around us that our hands take hold of in activity of will. Our breath and pulse are faithful indicators of our feeling life, as may be seen in the way both leap with joy and enthusiasm or seem to stop when we feel frightened or experience deep sorrow.

Now if it is true that man is related to the threefold plant as we have described, this fact has important consequences for a nutrition. Honey, cane and beet sugar have a stimulating effect on the corresponding bodily parts: the metabolism, the rhythmic system, and the nerve-sense organism (the physiological bases of soul functions).

We have to keep in mind here that sugar is a substance emancipated from the stream of the living plant and found as a deposit in blossom, stem-foliage and root. It may therefore be said to have withdrawn to some extent from the plant kingdom and taken on something of the mineral. In the white crystallized sugar turned out by refineries we have a highly denatured plant product almost close enough to the mineral to belong with salt. We might say, therefore, that all sugars add a salt-like component to the diet.

Sugar is in this sense a food that strengthens the soul and gives it a wholesome ego-awareness. It enhances personality. It is interesting in this connection to study tables of sugar consumption by the various nations:

Sugar consumption per person, in kilograms (taken from Ullmann's *Encyclopedia of Technological Chemistry*)

	1903	1914
England	46·4	40·8
America	32·0	33·6
Switzerland	20·7	34·0
France	20·1	17·7
Germany	19·5	34·1
Austria	10·6	17·0
Russia	6·7	13·3

Not only does sugar show a time-correlation with man's developing consciousness, with enhanced individual awareness, but there is also a geographical axis to the graph, indicating that sugar consumption varies from place to place in accordance with the prevailing state of consciousness. The western world, with its strongly developed individualism and intellectuality, consumes sugar in quantities many times greater than the East, where, at the time the measurement was made, the old patriarchalism still survived.

Today there are quite a number of new forms of sugar. Health food shops supply various kinds of raw brown sugar, which have not been subjected to chemical washing at a factory and may therefore be said to have escaped the denaturing which crystallized white sugar always undergoes. Brown sugar comes from all kinds of sources: sugar cane, sugar beets, the sugar palm, the sugar maple, and so on.

Dextrose, which is also known as glucose and grape sugar, is produced by treating starch with sulphuric acid. It is therefore a highly denatured product, as the tongue can testify. It is chiefly used in the making of candy and confections.

CHAPTER TEN

Salt in the Diet

'Salt is a marvellous thing' wrote Friedrich Christian Oetinger, a contemporary of Goethe, in his work on salt. 'It is possessed of the loftiest and most glorious nature, and is God's greatest, sublimest work in the whole realm of nature. There is nothing material that can compare with it. It is a subject and a mystery never yet penetrated, and never to be fully penetrated.'

Alchemists – and more recently Oetinger – were aware that salt came into existence as an expression of the formative force that permeates the universe, shaping world and man. They knew that salt forces worked hand in hand with the creative wisdom active in the world before matter took on final form and solidified. When this force was condensed into material salt, it 'grew stupid'. But it grows wise again on being digested and becoming part of us. Put another way, it might be called the foundation on which we can develop wisdom.

When salt crystals are put in water, we see a constantly changing flow of transparent forms emerging from their plane surfaces and merging with the solvent. The salt present here has lost its form, but we may say that it has awakened from its former state of sleep and become chemically active. It now exerts osmotic pressure and behaves exactly like a gas. We are not in a position to follow its further transmutation into wisdom with scientific means of observation, though a study of high dilutions does give us some idea of this spiritualization process.

Alchemists had other ways of knowing about the spirit inherent in salt. And when they described it as possessing three different aspects, they did so in their typically picturesque way of stating things: 'When we take salt processes into ourselves in foods, salt surrenders its sulphuric fire-spirit to the metabolism. It serves circulation by dispatching its mercurial spirit into the coursing motion of the blood. But it is in the head that salt's wisdom is freed.'

In our discussion of the history of nutrition, we saw that the consumption of foods from the mineral kingdom represents the third and last stage, 'nutritional modernity', and that this goes hand in hand with the development of individuality as it grows strong enough to digest minerals by raising them three steps to the human level. We are only just at the beginning of these modern times. And when we spoke of an increasing human capacity for digesting minerals, we meant, not so much that more and more mineral foods would be consumed, as that our digestive processes would tend increasingly in the wise direction in which salt can guide them. We will attempt to elucidate this in what follows.

Even materially, salts are a most important human food. We put salt into things not only to give them flavour but to help us think. Rudolf Steiner tells us that a person so ill that he cannot digest salt and who therefore lets it be deposited in his digestive tract becomes stupid to the point of feeble-mindedness.

How should we demonstrate salt's ascent to the brain? How do plant's sublimate their salts out into the universe on fading and how do they make sugar? They stream out as colour, scent and pollen on the wings of hydrogen into the warm mantle of the earth's atmosphere (cf. *The Nature of Substance*). A study of high dilutions or 'potencies' gives us a very similar picture of a gradual dematerialization on the part of salt, which finally reaches a condition of pure warmth.

Observe how salt starts dissolving on the tongue. Then it is caught up in the whole course of digestion continuing on through the stomach and intestines, becoming ever more finely dissolved or potentized, until it 'fades' through the intestinal wall into a purely spiritualized condition. The illness called 'salt fever' shows how warmth processes prevail here. A formative spiritual warmth streams by way of the heart to the brain, chiefly to its frontal parts.

Have we really quite appreciated the remarkable fact that salt itself has no taste, yet brings out flavour in foods on which it is sprinkled? C. Remer points out that we can only tell whether a dish is salted by the spiciness and smooth blending of aromas rising from it. For salt is selfless in the same sense as light, which illuminates everything it falls on while remaining itself invisible. This quality ranks it with the selfless thought which, in a search for knowledge, seeks not its own but rather brings light and order to the inner scene.

Despite all that may be said in praise of salt, however, and despite its great importance as a food, the following facts must also be added to the picture:

Taking salt in excess is harmful, especially in cases where an individual's ego forces are too weak to do the work of digesting it properly, for then it tends to form parasitical warmth-foci. Like poorly digested vegetable matter, which causes bloating, undigested salt collects in inflammatory pockets that have no natural place within the warmth organism. Consequently, each individual has to know for himself how much salt he can safely take.

The salts we eat come from all nature's kingdoms, but chiefly of course from the mineral realm. Cooking salt, which is composed almost wholly of sodium chloride, contains very small amounts or traces of calcium, potassium and magnesium salts. But by far the greater part of the calcium salts so essential to a properly nourished state occur in the water we consume. This makes it imperative to preserve them by the right cooking methods. This will be thoroughly discussed in a later chapter.

Potassium salts are taken up chiefly in vegetables. Plant ash contains up to seventy percent potash. We have to remember here that plant potash, though chemically identical with that found in minerals, is qualitatively quite different, being one step closer to the vegetable kingdom.

The salt that typically occurs in animals is that of sodium. It is present in every organ and in all the body fluids, particularly blood. When we eat foods of animal origin, we therefore consume large quantities of the sodium chloride that has been lifted close to the animal kingdom. This is especially true in the case of meat.

Magnesium salts, lastly, play an important rôle in man's physiological processes. They are found actively represented in plant processes as well as, for example, in assimilation by means of chlorophyll or in germination. But they form a particularly vital part of man's whole structure and play a vital rôle in his human functioning. Infants consume quite considerable amounts of them in their mothers' milk.

All salts, and indeed everything in the nature of a salt, serve literally as food for thought. They rise up as a stream of warmth that passes through the heart and stimulates the cerebrum especially. But each of the four salts discussed above gives the mental activity thus quickened a different colouring. We will discover what this is by studying each salt's function, both in the human organism and outside it.

In *The Nature of Substance*, calcium was described as having a special affinity to physical space. It is a very vital element in the earth's structure, and its stability assures the earth of a solid footing. In man, it is the agent of consolidation. It supplies the main ingredient of supportive tissue, causes blood to coagulate and proteins to harden. Calcium processes are active wherever the living element is undergoing metamorphosis into a solid. Their final achievement is the skeleton.

We must turn to plants to understand potassium. It is present in large quantities in fruit. Its tendency to encourage the colloidal state by helping to form surfaces, points to its connection with all vegetative processes. As I showed in *The Nature of Substance*, the coagulating element and the capacity to build sheaths to house some function that requires such an enclosure are native to potassium. Thus we find potassium processes at work in the human organism wherever organs are taking shape from body fluids. The vital qualities of these organs are potassium's contribution, as can be seen in the liveliest metabolic organ: the liver, which is also the richest in potassium. This organ plays the central rôle in what we have referred to as body chemistry, the living flow of body fluids. As G. Suchantke put it, 'Calcium rigidifies us, while in potassium we sense the fluid human being building solid organs out of the coursing stream of liquids'.

Sodium, for all its similarity to potash as a chemical, has its own very special nature, viewed biologically. It is the characteristic salt of the animal kingdom. And quite unlike calcium, which is constantly creating solids out of liquids, sodium causes no deposits whatsoever. It works exclusively in the body fluids of living creatures as an excitant. It stimulates muscles, nerves, procreation, everything that belongs in the realm of instinct and motion, in short, the sum total of animal nature. Thus we find the soul functions in man also related to sodium processes in his organism. The kidneys, with the kidney-stimulated functions of breathing and excretion which form the physiological basis of soul activity, clearly show a connection with common salt. And the lungs which we have described as a product of the above-mentioned minerals favour sodium, a fact that has been borne out in recent years by the discovery that sodium plays a very definite rôle in pre-disposing to tuberculosis. That is the reason why the Gerson diet withdraws salt from tubercular patients. And certain inflammatory kidney ailments also make a salt-free diet advisable.

Calcium, then, lends the body firmness, while potash takes part in building up the organs and their vital functions from body fluids. Sodium, as Suchantke points out, helps the air organism achieve the necessary stimulation of the life processes.

Magnesium is a very special kind of salt. The French clinician Delbet has uncovered highly interesting facts that allow us to gain a deep insight into the workings of this substance. Systematic research on the amount of magnesium in the various organs has shown that they can be rated as active or sluggish according to whether they contain much or little magnesium. Magnesium's relationship to calcium in the organs is particularly revealing. A comparison of bones as passive organs with muscles as active ones produces the following ratio:

| Bones | 1 Magnesium to 80 Calcium |
| Muscles | 2 Magnesium to 1 Calcium |

It would thus appear that the ratio of magnesium to calcium determines the degree of an organ's activity. An organ with a preponderance of magnesium is more pliable and active, and has a developmental or growth function. Growth and development are actively in progress when, in spring, seeds germinate and plant archetypes press into visible form as they send out shoot after shoot. The magnesium process is responsible for all this sprouting (cf. *The Nature of Substance*).

Similarly it is responsible for the unfolding of the human organism. We can see this especially clearly in the rhythmic course of youthful development, with its seven-year cycles.

Children spend their first seven years building their bodies and establishing their individual biological patterns. Each makes his bony system and his organs into an approximation of his own designing, bringing this work to a finish with the breakthrough of his second teeth, which magnesium has hardened. They are the last and hardest product of his body. But the same moment witnesses the freeing of forces that were previously tied to organic functions. They now go over into the service of thinking and memory, preparing the child for a formal schooling.

This transfer, again the work of magnesium processes, is one of human maturation's deepest secrets. Sending children to school or making them memorize a lot before its completion is a crass misreading of developmental fact. Unfortunately, this revenges itself on the child in later life in the form of illness caused by depleting the organism of forces which were needed to build up the organs properly, but were used up prematurely in mental effort.

The next period of life, during which children are developing reading and writing skills, is that of an unfolding of soul capacities. In their proneness to love and reverence, children of this age seek out someone to model themselves upon, are interested in mythology and the heroes of old, and have a strong feeling for history's great figures. A child unable to develop powers of reverence at this period becomes an empty soul in his old age, says Rudolf Steiner, and lacks the wisdom and serenity that could have proved a blessing for all who knew him.

Puberty terminates this period. And here again magnesium plays the major rôle, activating the reproductive glands, while the thymus or growth gland (one of the richest in magnesium) is inhibited. What does this period contribute?

We can watch how, as the body becomes more active, there is a budding interest in achievement. The young person reaches out for his goal in life, and seeks to realize his powers in individual creative action. And again, behind this development, a magnesium process is at work. Young people of twenty-one, we say, have 'come of age', meaning that the ego has fully manifested.

It is most interesting to find changes in the warmth organism going hand in hand with these rhythmic shifts of the developmental impulse. This should not surprise us, for we know that fire is maturation's native element (cf. *The Nature of Substance*). So we see magnesium serving the human ego and using warmth processes, first in the form of bodily growth, then as love on the level of the soul, and finally as a spiritual urge to accomplishment (cf. The writings of G. Suchantke).

The four salts described above together form a whole, reflecting laws that govern man and universe. The facts may be summed up thus:

Calcium salts	Mineral	Earth	Physical body
Potassium salts	Plant	Water	Life body
Sodium salts	Animal	Air	Soul
Magnesium salts	Man	Fire	Ego

Readers may recall what was said in *The Nature of Substance* and in earlier chapters of this book about the comprehensive nature of the Aristotelian elements. They embrace four cosmic forces, which manifest on many levels: in the natural kingdoms, in the systems of organs that co-operate to produce complete and healthy human protein, and in the four elements of protein: carbon, oxygen, nitrogen and hydrogen. Vitamins A, B, C and D are also forces springing from the same source and not as yet condensed to matter. They are also the reason why four substances: proteins, fats, carbohydrates and salts, are the mainstays of our diet. The physical body is built of protein; biological activity is based on fat; carbohydrates support the life of consciousness and feeling that lifts us above the merely vegetative; and the ego has its correlate in salt. Then, the four main systems of organs: lung, liver, kidney and heart systems, are also based on the same four-fold reality. However, I would remind readers that I refer to imponderables – forces, areas of activity, not just to physical substances. The act of breaking down and digesting foods frees the forces inherent in them, forces related, as described above, to the various complexes of organs. Material nutrients are thus transformed into forces that nourish the nervous system and the brain. Proteins and fats tend to act on the hind-brain, carbohydrates on the mid-brain, and salts on the fore-brain. These in turn act on the rest of the organism. It is of the greatest importance that thorough research be done into every detail of these processes, for only then will we have the right slant on many a question of health and illness.

We have tried above to give some idea of the hidden design underlying all of creation. Since man has a creative part in it in his digestion, it is time for him to recognize the cosmic forces with which he is dealing.

I could easily be thought to subscribe to the view that 'you are what you eat'. That is a mistaken interpretation of the facts presented. The personality or ego is the primary force in all questions of nutrition, and they are decided by the way the ego acts on bodily processes and masters or is mastered by them. Even the most carefully worked out diet will not help a man to 'eat his way into heaven'. Rather is the reverse true: food is a support that can be made use of only to the degree that the individual spirit actively transforms it.

CHAPTER ELEVEN

The Threefold Plant

Plants develop according to a bi-polar pattern. Their growth is due to the assimilation that takes place in their middle zone. Like the rainbow, which spans the poles of light and darkness, starch is formed in the plant's green foliage between the polarities of earth and cosmos, light, air and water. If the author may be allowed a personal reminiscence here, the primal phenomenon of starch formation burst upon him once when, on a journey to Australia, the ship ran into a monsoon. The day was brilliantly sunny, and the sun shone through the flying spray that enveloped the ship. The whole visible world became a rainbow-coloured bowl. The phenomenon might be called an everyday experience in a certain sense, considering the fact that rainbows in the sky or around fountains and waterfalls are equally effects of inter-acting light, air and water. Yet this experience in the middle of a remote and lonely ocean was so overpoweringly beautiful as to make the interested perceiver leap to the thought-conclusion: rainbows are the work of air, light and water! But starch too is formed of these very elements: air (carbon dioxide), light and water. The fact that heavy air (carbon dioxide) is involved in starch formation has the effect, in conjunction with the plant's life processes, of making assimilation more than just a show of colour: it progresses to the stage of material condensation into starch. The plant physiologists' formula for this, which reads

$$6CO_2 + 5H_2O \rightarrow C_6H_{10}O_5(\text{starch}) + 6O_2$$

is very interesting to chemists, but gives no clue whatever to the real story. A person who realizes that virgin starch is a condensed rainbow comes to a new sense of kinship with plant creation.

After the sun has finished forming starch in the plant's green foliage, this substance undergoes many further changes. Warmth and other environmental forces bring the plant past the leafy stage and into blossom, while starches are refined to sugars. Starch and sugar are close relatives, both being classed as carbohydrates, but sugar is a much more refined, etherealized carbohydrate than is starch. Chemists call starch a polymerized sugar. But this is only a way of saying that the two substances belong in one chemical category, with starches representing denser and sugars finer stages of the same.

After blossoming, great changes come over the substance of the plant. Blossom tissues become increasingly ethereal. Sugars become glycocides and make up the plant's colour. Scents develop, and the plant gradually disappears into the universe in an outpouring of radiance and fragrance. And the cosmos answers with a second materializing wave-crest that causes fruit to form and seeds to appear.

In *The Nature of Substance* I described in detail the many material transformations that take place as plants progress through the fruit and seed-forming phases of development and manufacture oils and protein. We will restrict ourselves here to pointing out one fact: that it is cosmic warmth and its etherealizing effect on starches that makes all this wealth of material transformation possible. We may therefore call the upper part of the plant its metabolic pole.

In contrast to this upward etherealizing, we find plant tissues more contracted the closer we come to the root. Here the earth's shaping forces harden the virgin substance, starch, to cellulose. Chemically it is still a carbohydrate, but a far denser form of it than is starch. This makes cellulose an excellent structural material, and we find it throughout the plant as framework. In the root it hardens almost to a wooden state, as can happen also in the stalk. The root area of plants may therefore be called their form pole.

The plant is thus a threefold organism developing from a creative central point of growth toward two opposite extremes: the form-giving, framework-building root pole, and the fruit-and-blossom metabolic pole.

Tracing these same elements in human beings, we come upon a similar threefold structure. In man, the form-pole is the head. No other part of the body can equal it in physical hardness and individuality of form. It is the source of all the formative tendencies that shape the organism, with the brain and the nerve-strands radiating from it playing a very important rôle. We all know that where nerves are severed, the affected part atrophies. There is no reason to ascribe this to deficient nutritive activity there. The fact is rather that formative impulses normally present in the part are missing, along with the nerve functions described in the chapter on cosmic nutrition.

Man's metabolic pole, unlike the plant's, is the lower one, and it is literally what the word means: transformer of substances. Where the plant transforms substances in its blossom area as a result of macrocosmic influences, the microcosmic human metabolism takes up and works upon the nutritive stream, transforming it into blood. In both cases, warmth is the agent of this transformation. In plants, the warmth is of cosmic origin, while in man, it is the microcosmic warmth of his own blood. So we find in man the same polarity of form and substance that the plant has, but reversed. This was to be expected, considering the fact that man grows down, not up, as the plant does. In the foetal period man is largely a head, with his other parts mere attachments, as it were. Even a new-born baby's head is proportionately much larger than a grown-up's, and it does not grow significantly later, but remains more or less as it was in the beginning. The trunk and limbs grow tremendously by comparison. These facts confirm our view that man grows downward.

The middle zone in man, where breathing and blood circulation are situated, corresponds to the leafy area in plants, the difference being that the human rhythmic functions have a far more comprehensive job to do than foliage. Their main responsibility is that of harmonizing the two poles of form (head) and substance (the metabolism). Thus they play the decisive rôle in health and illness.

When the head and metabolic poles are in balance, a man is healthy. He falls ill when imbalance sets in and the rhythmic middle zone is unable to correct it. Illness invariably comes from a disturbance of the normal balance, and healing always means restoring it.

Healing can be effected in two ways: either by strengthening the rhythmic man, the natural healer, or by giving such medicines or diet as will bring the down side of the scale up again.

Sometimes the form-pole gains the upper hand and breaks

through the middle zone in a way disturbing to the metabolic functions. This is one cause of illness, and we find under this heading all the hardening conditions like gout, rheumatism, stone formations, and sclerosis. People with these afflictions are usually thin, intellectual, nervous types.

To restore balance, the metabolic pole must be given the strengthening it needs to push the overweening nerve-sense pole back where it belongs. Medicines can be given, but there are also dietary means of helping. In cases of this sort, foods derived from the upper portions of the plant, i.e., fruits and blossoms, best activate the metabolism, for they are formed by forces related to those operative in the latter. Later on we will discuss how they should be prepared.

People also fall ill from the opposite condition of imbalance, where the metabolism overwhelms the nerve-sense system. All the numerous inflammatory illnesses belong in this category. Migraine, for example, is simply an intrusion of digestive processes into the head, which means that warmth, which rightly belongs to the metabolic realm, invades a region where coolness should obtain. This causes inflammations that can range all the way from boils to such serious illnesses as meningitis.

Treatment of this type of illness involves a strengthening of the nerve-sense pole. Root vegetables like beets and carrots, salsify, radishes, celeriac and turnips, which are related to the same formative forces operative at this pole, are the proper diet, and the rhythmic system mediating between the nerve-sense system and the metabolism can also be strengthened by a dietary emphasis on leafy vegetables. Fresh salads, spinach, sorrel and the like should be well represented in the meals served to patients with a lung problem or any other weakness of the rhythmic organism.

But the good effects of green leafy vegetables are by no means limited to patients in these categories. The rhythmic system is the seat of healing forces in the organism, for its function is that of a balancer and harmonizer. Green vegetables stimulate and strengthen these forces, and therefore make especially wholesome foods (Fig. 8).

The relationship between the threefold plant and threefold man comes into sharper focus when we consider the different ways people handle the different parts of plants. Take a person picking up a petal, for example: he will never hold it between his fingers, but lay it flat on his palm, probably lifting it a little in an instinctive reaction to its lightness, and smiling while he does this. Blossoms reveal their true nature in their fleeting perfumes; we

Fig. 8
The relationship of the formative forces
in plants to those in man.

sense something of their being as the scent rises up and disappears. Such a realization also tells us something of the therapeutic forces inherent in the blossom element. Blossoms are the parts of plants where sugar is found and where cosmic warmth etherealizes physical matter. They are thus able to affect that part of man where his own metabolic warmth processes etherealize what he has eaten and prepare it for use by his ego. Blossoms overcome gravitational drag on the metabolism and adjust food substances to the individual life-forces of an organism. The blossom element represents in nature the point at which purely vegetative processes are halted and breakdown sets in. For this reason blossoms act as stimulants to man's excretory functions. They drive warmth processes outward to the periphery and dissolve and sweep away congested heat as we can observe with fevers. Their chief effect is on the kidneys, which are themselves in a sense blossoms become organs. Blossoms are also more interesting to us than a leaf is. They attract our attention with their brightness, and we feel a warm reaction to their beauty.

How different is our attitude toward leaves! Picking up a green leaf, one observes that it is all one unmoving surface, each leaf with an individual twist to the one basic circular or drop-form pattern. If the liquid principle prevails, the shape is rounder, like a quiet pool, whereas a prevalence of light forces, with their pricking activity makes for a saw-toothed or feathered edging.

The first reaction a person has on coming into the presence of a green sea of foliage after sole contact with the rocky earth element is to take a deep breath. The breathing organism is stimulated when we enter a green forest and sense the breathing going on there in the foliage. A leafy diet has the same result. Trees are the earth's lungs, and rustling leaves their breathing.

Turning our attention to the realm of roots, we find permanent forms built by mineral processes, in greatest contrast to the ever-changing forms of foliage. Roots are wrought by processes that have come to a relative degree of stillness. If we catch a person studying a root, we will see how he wrinkles his forehead and contracts his brows, turning the object this way and that like Hamlet contemplating Yorick's skull. One feels particularly challenged to find out what the secret of this form is, for matter is more than usually mysterious here. Then too, plant roots, especially the more thick-set kind, always suggest faces and make us want to carve on them. They may be compared to the head of man. Roots therefore work on the nerve-sense organism, on forming the brain. Leaf and blossom are fairly limited to dynamic action, but in the case of roots there are also material effects. This makes it more important to consider the substances of which they are composed.

To understand the nature of a fruit, we must keep the following in mind: Fruits are not produced in direct continuation of the blossom process, but are the result of an answering cosmic radiation. Cosmic warmth and light form fruits and bring them to ripening. Here we are dealing with a quite different kind of substance than that found in other parts of plants. There is a parallel in man to this marvellous about-face from dematerialization in the blossom to the creation of fruit substances. The foods we consume do not just change directly into human substance but are diffused into the bloodstream, while on the other hand non-material elements (referred to by spiritual science as 'etheric forces') which enter us through our sense impressions are condensed into bodily substances. The creation of human tissue that goes on in the blood is a complicated interplay of earthly and universal forces, of which we have a picture in the fruit, itself a revelation of this double gesture on the plant level. We may therefore expect to find fruit having a more far-reaching effect than just on the intestinal functions: it also works on the circulation of man's body fluids. A sufficiency of fruits in the diet therefore stimulates blood and tissue building in a way that keeps the body 'fluid' in the widest sense, as well as permeable by cosmic forces.

One can go even a step further and say that fruit tissue is related to the seed in the same way that circulation is related to the heart. Ripe fruits are permeated by radiating cosmic light and warmth, but they are also made over into earth-related objects by their enclosing skins on husks and the contractive forces inherent in them, which are the actual cause of seed formation.

All the four cosmic forces or energies are concentrated in the seed: light and warmth in oil and starches, formative forces and chemism in salts and proteins. The two latter energies are the more dominant, and this accounts for the shape of the seed, which often looks like a tiny pebble. The process at work here has much in common with the circulatory process out of which the heart is formed – for the heart begins as a drop that is gradually imbued with matter. The contractive forces which in man cause cosmic spheres to become internal organs are the same as those which, in external nature, form the seed. Generally speaking, therefore, seeds have a warming, nourishing and 'heartening' effect. Juicy fruits have just the opposite *cooling* effect. They enliven and irradiate circulation.

We may sum up thus:

Roots	Nerve-sense system	Brain
Foliage	Rhythmic system	Lungs
Blossom	Metabolism and excretion	Kidneys
Fruit	Circulatory system	Blood
Seed	Organ formation	Heart

This approach helps to give a more intimate understanding of food qualities. But it is only a general outline. One has to acquire a perceptive eye for nature to read her secrets and arrive at true insight in each individual instance.

Then too, every plant does something just a little different with root, leaf and blossom processes. This means that though the above table gives an accurate summary, one can expect to find the same process worked out in a great variety of ways in all three sections of each single plant.

CHAPTER TWELVE

Milk and Honey

'The promised land, where milk and honey flow' has been the timeless yearning of the human race. But it is based on a true vision of wholesome living which might deserve the title 'human'. We would like to get to the bottom of this mystery.

Milk, as we have seen, is mankind's original and oldest food. It was manna from heaven at the time when earth's atmosphere (we refer here to Lemuris, the earthly repetition of the ancient moon-phase of the earth) was permeated with a milk-like protein substance, the last remnant of which is our present-day nitrogen. This was the beginning of man's earthly evolution. He started using the milk of his animals from the very beginning, and has continued to do so ever since. We see this period of evolution repeated in each individual's infancy and childhood.

Milk prepares the body for habitation by the soul and spirit. It brings a person down to earth and gives him a feeling for the oneness of the human race. Everyone among us breathes air that we own in common with our fellow men. Perhaps, buried deep within us, there is at work the memory of having partaken in common of a cosmic milk, that still gives us a sense of social bond between man and man. Rudolf Steiner tells us that in fact milk prepares man for being a creation of the earth, without preventing him from being a citizen both of the earth and of the whole solar system. To go without milk would estrange us from the earth and make us lose all connection with and feeling for man's earthly task. Therefore, says Rudolf Steiner, we do well, even as adults, to let ourselves be gently tied down here by taking milk.

So we find milk to be a help in incarnating properly and thus a suitable food during the first half of our lives.

And what of honey?

Plants, we know, refine their starches into the sugar found in their blossoms, and then further etherealize their substance into scent, radiant colour and wafting pollen. The further this sublimation has progressed, the more spiritualized are the substances involved, but the less alive. This may seem strange at first. But compare a flower's short life-span with that of a leafy shoot or a rugged root almost bursting with vitality. The green parts of plants regenerate without the least difficulty because they are in the life-zone, but this is not equally true of blossoms. I described in *The Nature of Substance* how hydrogen (there called 'fire substance') takes hold of plants at this point and carries them out into the cosmos on its pinions. Oxygen plays less and less of a rôle as metamorphosis brings the plant into and then beyond the blossom stage.

The honey stored in blossoms is therefore a very special substance. Though it has still not quite left the life-realm, it also has to do with the salt sphere – the salt we described as possessing wisdom. But honey's special quality is its closeness to the spirit, for it is produced in the area where plant substance is refined and metamorphosed into spiritual formative forces. It is both a physical and spiritual substance, permeated by salt's wisdom, which at this stage is closely related to the carrying quality of cosmic thought.

'Salt' in this context is not to be confused with root salts. For roots are of the materialization pole, a sphere where life loses its hold on salts and gravity claims them. But the mineralization (or, perhaps more accurately, the devitalization or falling to ashes) that takes place in the blossom area serves a heavenly, not an earthly end. At this point, substances become subject to higher, cosmic laws, which means becoming estranged from purely vegetative life. The spiritual salt process in the plant is therefore not the same thing as earthly, mineral salt, but consists of finely dispersed blossom elements such as nectar, scent, colour and pollen (cf. the section on Labiates in Chapter Fourteen).

The bees carry the nectar they gather into their selfless sphere, where everything is governed by a wise group-ego. People really able to appreciate the wisdom in a beehive's organization will sense a connection here with the human future. The fact that the temperature in a beehive is exactly that of human blood points to the activity in it of a co-ordinating ego similar to man's. And the wise will see in the bee's overcoming of sexuality, the pattern of developments to come.

Bees live in the world's breathing process. For the blossoms that pour out colour, scent and pollen are the world's organs of outbreathing, and the wise group-soul of bees has made them carriers of these substances. Honey is therefore a food that supports those human functions that help thinking to be felt and willed, and will and feeling guided by thinking. In the metabolic sphere honey stimulates the kidney action that we have found so vitally tied up with breathing and the nervous system. Indeed, honey has an ego-like capacity to work on man's organism and charge his blood with ego-like upbuilding impulses. It is an important food for older people, at the time of life when man's natural endowment of restorative ego forces is about exhausted.

Work with bees makes one receptive to inspiration from the bee's group spirit. The social forms that must be created before much longer will merge, in an illumined but still distant future, into simple love of our fellow men.

Honey thus has a deep connection with man's future development, as milk has with his past. And just as milk prepared us to enter earthly incarnation, honey prepares us to leave the earth when that time comes. Honey helps us to grow old gracefully and to ripen the wise fruits of living.

Individual lives and the history of the race as a whole run on strikingly parallel courses. Our statement (in the foregoing chapter on carbohydrates) that honey was used long before cane and beet sugar does not contradict this. On the contrary: the attitude of soul that prevailed in patriarchal times, when the group was everything and individual consciousness had not yet ripened, puts the individual creativity flowing into present culture into strong relief. Men of today are called upon to become creators in their own right, as the divine guidance that once ordered human affairs becomes the individual capacity of the human spirit.

Man acts upon the world and changes it with deeds of will. He will find that he has to give it a threefold social order consonant with his own threefold organism. The failure of the French Revolution to put its three ideals of liberty, equality and fraternity into full effect is not due to human frailty alone, but chiefly to the error of lumping all three ideals together in a common concept. Freedom can be successfully achieved only in the realm of cultural concerns, equality in the sphere of rights, brotherhood in economic matters. Culture, rights and economics faithfully reflect man's threefold nature in the social organism. And just as his own threefold organism suffers when metabolic processes encroach on the head, or nerve processes intrude into metabolic functions, the social organism sickens when the state, embodying the sphere of rights, interferes in cultural and economic matters, or economic interests try to set the tone of cultural life.

'The promised land where milk and honey flow' is not, however, just a pretty picture of the healthy, truly human way of living. Nor does it mean that one can set out on one's earthly path with a healthy start and grow old gracefully in wisdom and goodness. Up to the time of Christ the whole human race was concerned with coming down to earth. From that time forward mankind has been developing toward its earthly goal of maturity. The image embraces the whole planet Earth, with its beginning and its passing away.

CHAPTER THIRTEEN

Lily and Rose, Fruit and Grain

Lily and rose can both serve as representatives of the whole plant kingdom. Monocotyledons and dicotyledons (single and double petalled plants) are the two great classes of seed-bearing plants; lily and rose are the ultimate in their respective categories. Each is a queen in her own realm. The two may be said to dominate the plant kingdom as sun and moon the heavens. They have been symbols of special qualities from time immemorial and were sought after by the wise men of the orient. Zarathustra, the great initiate of early Persian days, taught his followers to breed the food plants that we still consider most important: fruits and cereals. The first are related to the rose, the second to the lily family.

All the various lilies have the six-pointed star of Zarathustra as their flower pattern. Tradition links lilies to the goddess Isis, and the so-called madonna lily is a Christian version of the same. Lilies are the plant of wisdom. Where they have been bred into food plants, as in the humble onion, leek, garlic, chives, and so on, they clearly reveal their link with the nervous system. The fragrance element of the blossom process permeates the onion through and through, extending its aroma and a certain rousing sharpness down into stalk and leaf. In its shape and substance too we see clear indications of the descent of heavenly forces through the entire plant. Thus it lends itself ideally to the rôle of digestive quickener. It 'aromatizes' those who partake of it, from inside out to their skin periphery. It stimulates excretion while at the same time helping soul and spirit to incarnate fully. Thus it proves itself an aid to the proper functioning of the two poles in man related to moon forces: brain and regeneration.

It is no coincidence that those oriental peoples most concerned with developing the brain as the organ of earthly reason, the Chaldeans, Sumerians and Semites, are even today particularly fond of eating onions.

In a narrower sense, the grasses from which grains were developed are also related to the lily family. Though breeding of true lilies developed onion forms, in the case of cereals seed-formation was the object. This has given cereal species a sun-related universality, even though they are offshoots of the lily family. They provide us with carbohydrates in the form of starches: sun-charged foods that show their universality in that

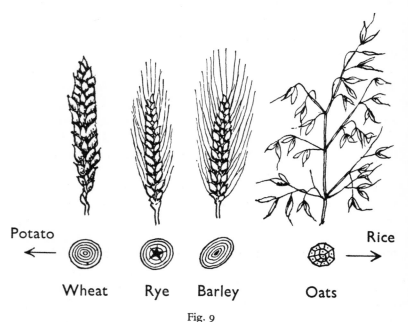

Fig. 9

The nature of the four types of grains and its expression in the smallest details of their form, the starch kernels.

grains, like all seeds, contain proteins, oils and salts. That makes 'our daily bread', practically as well as symbolically, *the* human food.

Wheat, rye, barley and oats are the grains known and grown in Central Europe. They are all wind-pollinated, meaning that air currents rather than insects do the work of pollination. Cosmic soul-being, active in the atmosphere and in bees, butterflies and other insects, touches plants, and they respond with a glorious wealth of colour. With grain there is no such actual touching, but only a general mingling with the soul-like airy element. This gives cereals a special aspect, considering the goodness and wisdom

inherent in the soul-being of the cosmos, which we have identified above with Isis-Madonna.

The grains to which we have ascribed these qualities represent
one fourfold organism made up of the four cereals wheat, rye,
oats and barley. In *The Nature of Substance* I pointed out the fact
that the cultivated plants from which starch is derived: potatoes,
wheat and rice, also represent a kind of earth-spanning organism.
Formative principles active in the plants themselves, in the tiny
grains of starch, and in the landscape, range from a western
tendency to harden into matter to an eastern radiating such as
typifies the element of warmth. Wheat, the most representative
cereal of the middle section, can stand for barley, oats and rye as
well. The way they all look and grow clearly expresses, even in
the tiniest detail of their forms, that they fit into a global patterning.

Wheat has the most compact form of all four cereals, while
oats, with their loose arrangement of berries and the radial
formation of their starch kernels, grow in a way reminiscent of
rice.

Water and air link the two opposite poles of soil and warmth.
Rye and barley actually occupy such a position between wheat and
oats. The elements identified by Aristotle are not more than just
the 'aggregate states' of modern physics: they are reflections of
ancient earth conditions, and should properly include the higher
elements light, sound (chemism), and life (the formative element).

Earth – Form	Wheat	rich in calcium salts
Water – Tone	Rye	rich in potassium salts
Air	Barley	rich in silicic acid
Fire	Oats	rich in magnesium salts

We see in the Table above how this grain foursome fits into
creation's building plan. Such is the case with other foursomes
too. Examples are presented by the four salts described in Chapter
Ten, by the four systems of organs, by the four protein elements,
and others will be met with in chapters to come.

The characteristics noted above make our four chief grains
excellent dietary aids in overcoming imbalances of the four
temperaments. Melancholics take to oat confections because of

the warmth-forces they contain. Those who know horses say that oats have the effect of making them fiery. And Germans say of excessively high spirits, 'that fellow has been stung by oats'. Today, oats can be had in many attractive and nourishing forms besides that rather phlegmatic old-timer, porridge. They are now made up into flakes, flour and groats. Cholerics, just the opposite of melancholics, like wheat or rye, and sometimes let themselves be weighted down with dumplings.

The fact that cereals contain proteins, oils and salts in addition to carbohydrates makes them the best all-around building food. Looking at percentages of the above nutrients, we find:

Cereal	Protein	Fats	Carbohydrates	Salt
Wheat	10%	1%	75%	Ca
Rye	11%	2%	70%	K
Barley	12%	3%	69%	SiO_2
Oats	13%	6%	67%	Mg

Oats have a conspicuously high oil content, but this will not surprise readers of *The Nature of Substance*, familiar as they already are with the fact of oil's fire-nature. The above examples illustrate the marvellous interplay of basic gestures of creation. We see, moreover, how consistently forces of a higher order carry out the universal plan as they shape the lower orders into organisms wherein the primal gesture constantly recurs.

Lilies and the cereals related to them are, as we found, offspring of the moon principle, the regent of wisdom and governor of nerve processes. A study of the rose, however, shows that it bears the sun's signature.

Due to the sun forces which they embody, plants of the rose family have an entirely different relationship to earth from lilies. They even grow into very large trees, bright with a glory of pentagonal blossoms in purple, rose or white. Light and darkness intermingle in them. Red roses have the colour of irradiated blood, of darkness redeemed by complete suffusion with the light element.

The fruits of today are all descendants of the rose. They possess nutritive qualities very different from those of cereals in that they do not build tissue but instead help body and spirit work harmoni-ously together. Circulation is the physiological basis of this function as the blood alternates between downward densifying and upward sublimation. Fruit thus nourishes our human-ness by linking our physical and our cosmic being. Its effect is felt in the life of our will and moral creativity.

Fruit feeds the circulatory processes and even has a direct part in making blood itself. Strawberries, for instance, are an excellent remedy for anæmia.

A study of the various fruits turns up many differences, so that even though the general rose character described above holds

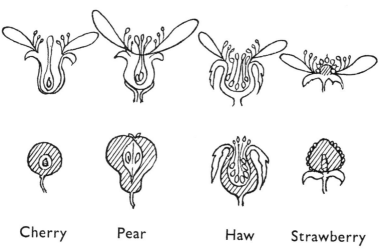

| Cherry | Pear | Haw | Strawberry |

Fig. 10
Fruit and seed formation of the four fruits related to the rose.

true for all, there are nevertheless distinctions to be noted, distinctions that play an important rôle in man's nutrition.

Here again there are four general groups of fruits: stone-fruits, seed-bearers, haw-fruits and berries. The way a plant sets fruit and seed always seems expressive of its underlying character.

The cherry, one of the group of stone-fruits that includes plums, apricots and peaches, has a single, isolated but beautifully formed pit that hardens and becomes a stone. The whole picture is one of self-sufficiency, even of something not too far removed from egotism. As though to make up for the pit's contraction, the fruit fills out around it and is plump and juicy. But caution has to be observed with stone fruits. An old saying warns, 'Don't drink water when you're eating cherries!' Sensitive stomachs even develop nausea from it. This is perhaps due to the aversion the cherry has to water. A study of its kernel proteins shows cyanide to be very active in it. This is evidence of a contractive, hardening process that goes so far as to affect protein formation in the seed, causing the element of living water to dry up and turning the proteins poisonous in consequence.

Strawberries, quite the opposite, open without reserve to their surroundings. Their red fruits are the product of the adnation of the ovaries growing together, and the many tiny seeds are deeply embedded in the juicy, full receptacle. This little berry with its appealing fragrance and its cheery red makes a friendly and modest impression. Raspberries and blackberries are similar.

The kernel fruits and haws occupy the two median positions which form a bridge between the opposite poles of cherry and strawberry.

Let us take the pear to represent the group of kernel fruits, which includes apples, medlars, quinces, whitehorn and the mountain ash. This is a less imposing fruit than peach or cherry. The pistil is made by a union of five carpellary leaves, with two seeds apiece, which form the core, and the juicy flesh grows out of the ovary and the stem tissue, which have grown together.

Haws have numerous pistils, all contained within a common receptacle. But they have not as yet followed the strawberry's lead in turning their receptacles inside out. Haws have a motherly way of enwrapping the pistils, while their styles, with their bright yellow stigma, radiate out from the receptacle like beams of light. Rosehips look like products of light and, as we know, have a high count of Vitamin C, which we called 'latent light' in *The Nature of Substance*.

Grains bear the clear imprint of the elements in their morphology. They are body-builders, and as such affect the temperaments associated with the body. In the case of fruits, however, one can easily gain the impression that they are moral qualities reflected in matter.

The lily and the rose have the same relationship as nerves and blood. The latter are kept cleanly separated, physiologically, for if they touched, illness would result. It is of prime importance that each function independently, keeping to its own set of laws, yet in harmonious co-operation with each other. It may not be at all far-fetched to remind our readers here of the English War of the Roses, really a war between the lily (the white rose) and the red rose. It raged for decades, not only decimating the aristocracy of York and Lancaster, but all the youth and culture of the period. It takes quite a bit of doing on a lofty level to unite the lily and the rose or to transform one into the other.

There is a legend that recounts how St Elizabeth, Countess of Thüringen, daily visited the poor and ill against her husband's will, taking a basket of bread to give them. One day the Count surprised her on this errand, and behold, there were roses in her basket!

We have said that lily and rose related to each other as nerves to blood. Since the latter are the physiological basis of thinking and will, we can equally well say that lily and rose resemble thinking and willing. We are evermore compelled to infuse will into our thinking and thought into doing. What on the physiological level must be kept separate can be fruitfully united on the soul plane. Bread and fruit are the two foods which support such union. That honey furthers this spiritual breathing, this breathlike transformation and exchange, has already been mentioned.

Lily and rose are related as are bread and wine, for by transubstantiation they are consecrated as the body and blood of the Lord. There is an epigram about the rose which expresses this. Let it close this chapter.

> The flowers all bloom
> as ordained on high –
> they would they were roses.

> Men all strive
> in the presence of love –
> Sun, be on earth.

> Sun, teach me to be
> gentle as your rays,
> never ending.

NUTRITION

Rose, teach me to flower
in humanity
in thanks to God.

HERBERT HAHN

CHAPTER FOURTEEN

Legumes, Crucifers, Umbelliferae, Labiates

P roteins, fats, carbohydrates and salts were described above as
the four categories of essential foods required in the upkeep
of man's total being: physical body, life body, soul and ego. What
we mean is that they provide the necessary stimulus to the
functions that support man's soul and spiritual activity. Though
all plants consist predominantly of carbohydrates, the four above
categories are clearly represented by the four plant families that
are the subject of this chapter. This fact indicates their relationship
with the four parts of the human entelechy and man's four
systems of internal organs (cf. H. Walter).

LEGUMES

The legumes or papilonaceae, are a very strange family of
plants. Plants are usually exclusively vegetative, and have no
trace of animal characteristics or processes. Motion, which is
peculiar to animals and has its physical counterpart in protein (or
nitrogen), does not appear in the same way in plants, which cannot move from place to place. But an element of motion nevertheless enters the picture at a certain point in their development,
when bees, butterflies and other insects visit them. Here the
plant reaches up into the animal sphere just as at its opposite pole,
the root, it reaches down into the realm of minerals. At the upper
pole we see a most remarkable meeting of the pure life-realm of
plants with the soul element of the cosmos, represented by the
insects fluttering about them.

The result of this meeting is the blossom and the seed that
begins developing within it and producing the proteins which
might be called the shadow cast on plants by the sphere of
animals. This is as far as plants are meant to go in their contact
with that element; they are not equipped for any more-deep-
reaching penetration. As we showed above, poisonous plants are
the product of too deep an involvement with the animalic. The
plant poisons called alkaloids are simply distorted proteins, used-
up matter of an animal-like nature which plants cannot excrete as

animals do, but store within them (cf. *The Nature of Substance*, Chapter Fourteen).

It is surprising that legumes are not poisonous, for they have more animal aspects than any other plant. Their blossoms even look like butterflies held fast, which shows how far they have gone toward a union with the animalic element. Add to this the very high protein content in the seed, which comes from the ability of legumes to assimilate nitrogen directly from the air. There is a good deal of speculation about the bacteria in the root nodules which play a rôle in fixing nitrogen, but authorities disagree about their function and certainty on this matter is not essential to our presentation. Here, it is more to the point to describe plants of this kind, with their animal qualities and high protein content in a way that brings their archetype more to life.

Modern spiritual science does this. It provides concepts that cast light on many puzzling phenomena. The past evolution of the earth and its kingdoms has gone through stages only to be understood by seeing the past as it really was; we go astray if we picture them developing under conditions much like those of the present. Spiritual science describes, for example, how in times long past the moon was still part of the earth, and the plants on it quite different from anything we know today, for they had feelings of a kind and these could be stirred. At that time there were no extreme differences between the various natural kingdoms; plants were partly animal. The atmosphere was not dead as it is today. It was permeated by a finely dispersed living protein that had a semi-fluid, semi-airlike consistency. This cosmic 'milk' was the food of mankind in its infancy. Obviously the plant-animals of the period also lived on this protein atmosphere. When it began to lose its living quality after the separation of the moon and earth, and became the residue we know as nitrogen, evolution brought forth a series of tremendous metamorphoses. What had been external atmospheric processes were interiorized and centred in certain internal organs or other focal parts of living bodies.

It would seem that the nitrogen-fixing group of plants called legumes still keeps to the old primeval form of protein intake. The rest of the plant kingdom has transferred its reference wholly to the sun and uses sunlight to make the typical plant substance, starch, in its green foliage, out of water and carbonic acid. Legumes, however, have preserved the capacity plants once had to assimilate the dead nitrogen residue of the erstwhile living cosmic protein and enliven it into protein in their organisms. This latter part of the process is significant, for if legumes were unable to make living protein from the nitrogen absorbed they would all be poisonous.

They too, of course, have gone on to the green sun-stage of the plant kingdom. But he who looks with an artist's sensitivity at bean plants really gets the impression that he has an atavistic animal-plant before him as he sees the tiny butterflies called bean blossoms making their way up the stem and turning into seeds that in their final stage look just like kidneys.

The papilonaceae or butterfly-flowered species make up the group of bean-plants that are such an important human food source. It includes peas, lentils and soya too, and even clover, which, though we seldom bring it into the kitchen, is a most valuable cattle fodder and bee-food. The various clovers thus contribute indirectly to supplying man with his most important foods, milk and honey.

The acacia and golden shower or laburnum are also papilonaceae. Acacia blossoms baked in pancakes are a prime food favourite and very good for us. But caution is advised when it comes to eating golden shower: the atavistic capacity of legumes to enliven into a complete living protein the nitrogen they assimilate is a power golden shower no longer has. This makes every part of it poisonous.

The protein legumes contain is all in the seed. Here follows a comparison with seed of other plants:

| Grain | 10% protein |
| Legumes | 25% protein |

Peas, lentils and beans are foods included in the diet because they further the building-up of protein in the organs. They have the tendency, already noted with respect to excessive protein intake, of causing too great a degree of hardening, of making the body tissue dense and heavy and tying body and spirit too closely together. This, plus the wholly atavistic nature of legumes, was the reason why Pythagoras and his pupils avoided pulse foods. The protein they contain is more truly animal than milk.

The above considerations also throw light on the story of Esau, who sold his birthright for a mess of pottage. The picturesque language of the Old Testament describes Esau, in great contrast to the clever Jacob, as a primitive, shaggy, hairy fellow. We see in Jacob a personality in whom the power of individual egohood has already been at work developing the brain and an ability to think, while Esau represents the old adherence to a tribal spirit that has nothing to offer the future. He sells his rights as the first-born of his family for a mess of pulse or pottage because he is still wholly governed by the desire-nature rooted in his metabolism.

CRUCIFERS

The crucifers are entirely different from the legumes. This group can be recognized by their four petals arranged like the axes of a shining white or yellow cross. These plants are sturdily set in space and on the earth. Where they have been cultured into food plants they form heads, shaped so differently in every case that we see how alive and strong the plastic potentiality of this plant family is.

A pronounced sulphur process is common to all crucifers. We witness a great variety of matter being built up and transmuted in them, and sulphur is the agent here. Rudolf Steiner called sulphur 'the substance that the spirit wets its fingers with' when active in the world of matter. In *The Nature of Substance* I compared sulphur's warmth quality with that of a hen warming life into her eggs. Sulphur keeps the plastic growth forces of the crucifers so alive and capable of change that little new heads can be produced in every part of the plant. Cabbages show a great variety of head forms, all of which result from their capacity to keep on producing earthly substance. This plastic tendency can be encouraged, and it is the sulphur element so typical of them, that makes such a luxuriance of shapes possible.

Every housewife knows that the cabbage pot must be left open at the top to let the unpleasant sulphur smell escape in cooking.

Plants of the cabbage family form heads in all the various areas of a plant, from top to bottom:

Turnip	Root-head
Kohlrabi	Stem-head
White cabbage	Solid leaf-head
Red cabbage	Sweet leaf-head with colour
Savoy cabbage	Curly leaf-head
Kale	Curly open leaves
Brussels sprouts	Bud-heads
Cauliflower	Blossom-head

The various plants have the same thin blue-green wax layer on their leaves and stems that we find in all crucifers. This fact is significant, for wax formation is due to the sulphur process found also in the cosmic fire element active in seed and blossom, and responsible for the oils produced there. These latter are midway between fats and resins. All crucifer seeds are rich in oil.

Rape and turnip seeds are the chief source of vegetable fats and oils. The fatty nature of the crucifer family shows up clearly in the following comparison between the oil yield of wheat berries and rapeseed:

Wheat	1% oil
Rape	40% oil

Other members of this family reveal their sulphuric nature in that they metamorphose into sharp etheric oils, as is seen in the case of mustard, radish, cress and horseradish. These etheric oils, so rich in sulphur, are found not only in the seed and blossom parts of the above-named plants, but permeate their whole organism; in cress, they appear in the foliage, in radish and horseradish in the root itself. This lends to these species an almost therapeutic character, for their penetrative powers, when taken as a food, have a quickening effect on lazy metabolisms and free the nerve process in the head. Horseradish in particular has a distinct relationship to warmth processes that take place in the liver, in the secretion of gall. It relieves congestion in this area, and helps the ego forces to do their work of stimulating the necessary fire-processes of the metabolism. This eases the nervous system and helps overcome any tendency to migraine that may exist.

The inherent capacity to effect change in both form and substance which this whole plant family possesses shows its relationship to the chemical and plastic functions centred in the liver. While these latter encourage the building and depositing of matter and thus weight life down to some extent, they do so in the element of sulphuric warmth, thus quickening and firing the whole metabolism. Both tendencies are present in the crucifers, and the predominance of one or the other depends on whether the plastic or the chemical element predominates.

THE UMBELLIFERAE

The umbelliferae are all shaped alike. Though there are hundreds of plants in this family, they are as uniform as the crucifers are varied. This is something we can understand if we try to feel intuitively the way in which the umbelliferae grow. The leaves, reduced to little more than a rib structure, are arranged in spirals around a hollow, vertically-grooved stalk. This stalk soon splits up into a radiating spray that divides into further smaller sprays, tipped with tiny white or reddish five-pointed blossom-stars. The whole plant seems a creation formed by and of the element of light. The shape of its blossoms shows that light was the strongest of the formative forces engaged in its making, for the degree to which light participates shows up in the edges of the leaves. These vary greatly. Some are smooth, some indented, or saw-toothed, or feathered, while others have completely slit edges, like those of the umbelliferae. Light has the effect of dematerializing foliage, so that only the more resistant rib structure tends to survive. The green leaves and hollow stem are thus light-formed, and the inflorescence of the umbelliferae and the small size and delicacy of their blossoms both reveal light's share in their shaping. All umbelliferae have a strongly centrifugal, peripheral tendency quite different from the crucifers' tendency to emphasize physical differentiation.

It seems almost a miracle that these feathering plants have dense, bulky roots. Carrots, celeriac and parsnips are examples.

The materials of which these roots are composed, however, are also products of the light: sugar and starch, both carbohydrates. Carrots are sweet, and so, to some extent, are parsnips and celeriac. The flowerlike yellow of the carrot also indicates that cosmic forces normally active only in the region of the blossom have here penetrated to the very root.

The umbelliferae bring into sharp relief what has already been stated on the subject of carbohydrates as nutrients. They begin to take effect after the liquefied food has disappeared through the intestinal wall; at this point they support the upward climb of the nutrient stream. Man represents a continuation of the plant kingdom in the cosmic process, in that he first breaks down the plant matter he consumes, dematerializes it, and then builds his own nervous system out of the light-forces he has freed in this manner. For the light that forms plants in the outer scene is the force that, when interiorized, builds the structure of the nervous system.

The way umbelliferae are made shows how active light has been in them. These plants are good material for study, if one wishes to understand light's shaping rôle, in the human sense, and in the nervous organism.

This light-formed nerve-sense process in the upper man is reflected in his metabolic region in the break-down and excretory processes. The umbelliferae help these break-down products pass out of the body, further the secretion of sweat, milk and urine, thus making room for a health-giving penetration of the physical man by soul and spirit.

We can therefore understand why aromatic seeds of such members of the umbelliferae family as coriander, fennel, caraway and anis act medicinally in cases of insufficient carbohydrate metabolism, the blockage of movement in the air organism which produces bloating. Moreover, it is interesting to note that these are the seeds used to flavour bread and other baked foods.

Dill, chervil and parsley are valued as aromatic sauces for a wide variety of foods. Like all umbelliferae, they lift, lighten and support the upward flow of nutrients. Their effect is very much like that of spices and they can certainly be ranked among spring's blood-purifying herbs.

LABIATES

One gets the clearest impression of the labiates by tasting and smelling them. They all have a warming fragrance and flavour. The curious thing is that their flowers are not the only source of this aroma: it is as though the whole plant had been dipped in aromatic fire forces from root to blossom. Take a peppermint leaf, for example, and rub it between the fingers or chew it, allowing its special qualities of taste and smell to register deeply on one's senses. One feels flooded by a warm well-being, soothed and pulled together. Plants of this family are not the sort to whip up and stimulate. Each possesses in its individual aroma the power to calm and harmonize. They lighten heaviness, drive chills away, and relieve monotony, all effects that aid the metabolic forces.

Etheric oils are carriers of these harmonizing elements that permeate labiates, and they in turn owe this capacity to hydrogen, which I termed 'fire substance' in *The Nature of Substance*. Etheric oils are the richest in hydrogen of all plant substances. They lift toward the wide reaches of the cosmos as though on wings of warmth, raising the plant with them as they do so. Etheric oils are true mediators between 'being and appearance' in the Goethean sense. We lay hold of the innermost being of a plant in its perfume, and a whiff of its scent is enough to conjure up an image of its earthly 'appearance'.

There is a basic difference between the etheric and the fatty oils. The latter form only as the seed is ripening. Fatty oils are also rich in hydrogen, but they are the product of an answering radiation from the cosmos after the flower has undergone the dematerialization involved in developing fragrance and breathing itself out into the universe. Fatty oils are therefore saturated substances, with a direction toward rather than away from earthly life. They too contain warmth forces, but in the form of the highest plant-chemical synthesis, built, as salt is, of fatty acids and glycerine which represents the base in this combination. Fatty oils thus go in a totally opposite direction to etheric oils: like crucifers they hug earth, substances with a saltlike self-containment, cosmic warmth weighted down by matter. Burning of course liberates this warmth again.

One single gesture is common to all labiates: that of giving themselves out, going up in scent or aroma. The comparable in man is that of digestion as it takes place on the other side of the intestinal wall. Thus the labiates aid assimilation and transubstantiation processes in the blood; they accompany food substances as these are broken down from their initial 'appearance' or material state into one where they become pure force or being. Labiates then support the ego in its task of building up uniform human protein.

The various mints, melissa, marjoram, thyme and salvia, as well as rosemary and summer savoury warm the digestive tract through and through. And they are particularly effective in supporting the heart as it mediates between the upper and lower poles of the human organism.

It may seem surprising to find that some of the labiates which we have described as formed by cosmic fire forces have exceedingly massive, rectangular stalks, that the leaves, which form a cross of opposing pairs when seen from above, tend to be square or even cubic, something found in its full perfection only in the earthy salt. But fire and salt are not unrelated, and there is reason to regard the labiates as archetypal expressions of what we have referred to elsewhere as salt's wisdom. Though the labiate shape is wholly formed by earth's salt forces, fire forces do indeed permeate it from top to bottom. Then they rise up with that rhythmic alternation always characteristic of vital processes and are sublimated in the pungent aroma of etheric oils.

CHAPTER FIFTEEN

Nightshades

POTATOES AND TOMATOES

The nightshades are a family of poisonous plants which include belladonna, henbane, the thorn apple, nicotiana, and the popular tomato and potato so widely used as foods. I described in *The Nature of Substance* how plants become poisonous by allowing the animal (or soul) element to penetrate them too completely. Since plants are not organized by nature to include this element, the normal protein-forming process in the seed, which usually contains only a limited amount of nitrogen, takes the abnormal course of making alkaloids. The nightshades show their poisonous nature in their above-average content of nitrogen. And we even find an imitation of the gastrula, the basic form from which an animal develops, in the deeply carved cavity above the seed bud of all nightshade blossoms.

Now what ever persuaded humankind to make food plants of the tomato and the potato, every part of which is poisonous?

It is significant that neither plant is of European origin. The Spaniards brought both from America as curiosities. They are native of Peru, where they had been domesticated by the Aztecs. The Aztec name for tomato was 'tomatl', whereas the potato got its name in Europe, from truffels, 'tartuffoli', which it faintly resembles. The botanist Clusius planted the first European potato in 1588.

The discovery of America marked the beginning of a new phase of consciousness. Man went, so to speak, beyond the limits of his own personality, and started to probe into and lay hold on the external world through sense observation. He not only sought to discover and claim new territory, but to understand the laws of nature also. Potatoes and tomatoes may be viewed as foods which help the consciousness-soul take its first infant steps, for they stimulate the head's intellectual activity and bolster up a certain egoistic self-satisfaction. The price that had to be paid for this progress was a temporary sidetracking into a one-sidedly materialistic point of view, as we will try to explain below.

Potatoes are our chief source of carbohydrates and are grown in enormous quantities. In Germany alone, over fourteen per cent of arable land is devoted to potato raising. Science holds the potato in very high esteem as a source of calories and thinks of it as a good bulk food, not only because there is plenty for everybody but because it makes such a filling meal.

A comparison between the food values of wheat and potatoes shows up:

	Carbohydrates	Proteins	Fats	Water
Potato	18%	1·5%	0·1%	80%
Wheat	75%	10·0%	1·0%	10%

We see from the above how poorly the potato compares with cereals, and the picture is still more convincing with respect to its inner qualities. For though it is a starch-producing plant, its carbohydrates are not a seed product as cereal carbohydrates are, but a product of the root-tuber. This, as we know, relates them to the nervous system. The carrot and celeriac are also in this category, of course, and we have already pointed out what a beneficent influence they have upon the head. But quite different elements enter the picture in the case of the potato. For potatoes are nightshades, and have every earmark of this group of plants – a fact bound to affect the nature of potato starch, even though the difference is not readily demonstrable. However, artistic feeling for the facts can see the qualitative difference between grains of wheat and potato starch.

There is what we might call an inbred self-absorption in the kernel of potato starch, that compared with the harmonious, even structure of a grain of wheat starch, appears as distorted as does the protein development that makes alkaloids in poisonous plants.

Digesting carbohydrates of this kind is obviously not as smooth and easy a matter as digesting other plant substances. The stimulus carbohydrates give to the regeneration of the nervous system cannot be achieved so selflessly in digesting potatoes. Instead, even the brain is made to participate in this process. As Rudolf Steiner put it, 'We digest proper bread made of wheat or rye in the stomach and intestines and do not involve our heads in this function. But when we eat potato bread, or potatoes in any form at all, we will find that the head has to be drawn into helping digest them.'

We described above how carbohydrate foods are used chiefly to nourish the middle portion of the brain. This is the brain area that supports creative, artistic and imaginative thinking. If the middle brain is made to serve digestive functions, as it has to do after a meal of potatoes, it cannot do its proper work. Then the forebrain has to substitute for it. But this part of the brain is very

Starch Kernel of
Potato

Starch Kernel of
Wheat

Magnified approx. x 500

Fig. 11
Potato and wheat: their being is revealed in the forms they
take.

differently constituted, both as to cellular structure and in what might be called a localized capacity. These fit it for an entirely different function: that of serving the more materialistic thinking and consciousness of the present day, with their tendency to dry scientific abstraction. Creative thinking has declined in Europe since the potato was introduced and became so popular.

But there is more to it than this. We were at pains to show how carbohydrate foods go chiefly to support man's inner life, particularly feeling, and the capacity for motion that belongs with it. He needs soul capacities throughout his organism, and the carbohydrates found in wheat and rye supply them. But where potatoes are the only carbohydrate food his soul capacities are all imprisoned in his head. This makes him weak. Rudolf Steiner tells us he cannot work properly, for the spirit grows dull and sleepy when it is not provided with carbohydrates that act on the entire man. But when a potato diet has not only weakened a person to the point where hands and feet cannot serve him properly in the work he does, but in addition weakens the reproductive powers and organs, indeed he is by then even worse off. The human spirit connects itself with the physical germ at the moment of conception, and proceeds, as we know, to build up the body from the head, not only during the foetal period, but right up to the seventh year of childhood. It is therefore of the first importance that the spirit be able to penetrate the head properly. But in cases where an incarnating human being has to deal with an ovum in which the budding head has already been ruined by the father's or mother's one-sided use of potatoes, it is indeed hard for it to enter fully. This is the way hydrocephalus starts. Incarnation is a gradual process that proceeds in rhythmic intervals of seven years. It takes the first seven years for the physical body to establish itself, and it rounds out this period at the coming of the second teeth. Then follows a further seven year period during which the inner powers are developing. This is concluded at puberty. From fourteen to twenty-one, when a person comes of age, the ego is learning to master soul and body. When excessive potato eating has resulted in handing on a body that cannot be properly grasped by the spirit, normal maturation is prevented in these early years. Then, says Rudolf Steiner, 'a person goes through life almost as though he had no body, so limply does it hang on him'.

Thus we may say that a one-sided potato diet not only makes the brain too earthy but means that people are born too weak to meet the demands of living. When this goes on for generation after generation, as seems to be the case already, we need to have our attention called to the facts, unless we want to risk very serious degeneration.

It is most important to see to it that children are not fed too many potatoes. When they are sleepy, scattered and inattentive, it is advisable to check up and see whether they have not been eating more potatoes than are good for them. Sugar, vegetables and fruit, and the warming effects of caraway, thyme and horseradish, are the proper antidotes. There is an Austrian dish made of potatoes cooked with apple which is aptly named 'earth and heaven', a witness that healthy instinct senses something of the facts.

In view of the above, it is truly alarming to realize the extent to which the potato has come to be used in European countries. Kollath estimates that it accounts for twelve per cent of the total diet. This should be made the concern of political economists in future, for healthy social conditions may well depend on restricting the planting of potatoes.

It appears that the potato itself has undergone considerable degeneration as a plant. It is subject to a host of diseases, and could conceivably die out. History knows of many a cultivated plant that has done just this when its mission was accomplished. It might be putting the case more accurately to say that beetles have appeared because the potato's job is done and it must go rather than that its decline is due to the attack of the potato beetle.

Only in the last few decades has the tomato become a widespread food. The experts have dubbed it 'rich in vitamins' and health-food groups have taken it up and helped make it almost the basic vegetable. It is as frequently found in gardens as potatoes in the fields. It has every earmark of a nightshade except the poison. Looking at this plant and the self-assertion in its rank growth process, one feels an instinctive reserve toward it and should not be too surprised at hearing from gardeners that it is one plant that does best on its own compost.

Despite all the findings on vitamins and desirable chemical elements that weigh heavily in the tomato's favour, we must also weigh the imponderable impressions gained from a perceptive study of its deeper-lying qualities. Its rankness alone would make one hesitate to let a person threatened by cancer eat it. Before a person actually develops cancerous growths he goes through a prior stage of shutting himself off from life and having little interest in or loving relationship to his surroundings. He is the victim of an involutionary tendency that finally turns his forces inward in a rank physical proliferation. This is of course a long and complicated story, but it has aspects that remind one of a tomato's way of growing. Crystallization studies of cancerous blood and tomato juice show a very striking structural identity. Here we see, then, two members of the nightshade family accompanying us on a short stretch of our evolutionary journey. Both are gifts of the western hemisphere. They have helped us on our way through a materialistic phase that now leaves us a heritage of capacities which, if we lay hold on them, can be the foundation of a new scientific outlook – an outlook with a vantage-point from which we might approach the mystery of life with a new, wise power of understanding.

CHAPTER SIXTEEN

Seasoning Herbs and Spices

Seasonings have come into increasing use the more man's development has enabled him to enter into full possession of his body and experience it in all its inner differentiation. In Egyptian times, spices were used only by priest-kings. Later, royal courts followed suit. In the great days of Greece and Rome, they came into general but moderate use. The spice trade became a considerable business, especially in the hands of the Arabs. Spices commanded a very high price in the Middle Ages. Pepper, for example, came to play a rôle similar to that of gold. It was often used in place of money. Pepper customs were set up at borders, and kings and princes made each other presents of pepper.

The Middle Ages marked the start of a new focusing of man's mental powers on the material world. It is not too difficult to see how the new use of spices fitted in with this awakening of the senses as they were brought to bear more precisely, fully and discriminatingly on man's surroundings. Wherever the enhancement of consciousness was made to serve a sharper development of thought and concept, there were seasonings in the food and on the table. Every court and monastery vied for distinction in their skilful use. The change-over from a dreaming state of mind to full alertness of the senses, such as was now required for observation of the laws of nature, meant preparing and developing the body for this task.

A thorough study of seasoning agents shows that they occupy the halfway point between a food and a medicine. They are not regenerative in the sense that proteins, fats and carbohydrates are. On the other hand, neither are they specific remedies for any illness. Perhaps the best way to describe them is to rank them with salt, in the sense that salt is the basic means of bringing out flavour, and may therefore represent all seasoning agents. We found in our study of salt that it possesses the admirable quality of having no taste of its own, instead enhancing savour in the foods it flavours. In this it resembles light, which – itself invisible – makes visible that on which it falls. Salt is thus the basis of all taste. This in turn guides us to the basic character of seasonings: they bring out taste.

It is generally thought most inartistic cookery to let a seasoning be too obtrusive. The ideal is to apply a herb or spice in such a subtle manner that the food thus flavoured retains its distinctive savour but is 'toned' in a certain particular direction. Kitchens should therefore contain a variety of seasonings, and cooks become artists at blending them in an 'aromatic symphony'. The food and the seasoning thus complete each other.

All this indicates the close ties between seasonings and heightened awareness: awareness not only on the part of the cook but of those who eat the food he seasons. Awareness is sharpened by its flavour and aroma, and the more subtly the sense of taste has been aroused, the greater the interest that follows the food through the digestive process. We see what an awakening has taken place, even physiologically, and how a true art of spicing helps digestion by rousing a person's livelier participation.

In the chapter on salt, we described how this substance, properly digested, is brought up to the warmth condition and carried to the brain on the rising stream of nutrients, to support our thinking. Its power to awaken us is part of our enjoyment of the flavour of food. The herbs that join forces with salt to create taste symphonies are derived chiefly from plants that typify throughout the sublimating, mineralizing, salt and ash-forming process.

This we have shown to be true of the labiates. These aromatic, spicy-smelling plants pour out their fragrant being into the warmth organism of the cosmos. This tendency enables them to support analogous metabolic warmth-processes that proceed into consciousness in the system of the nerves and senses. One can describe all labiates as salt-related stages of metamorphosis on the way to what we have called 'the wisdom contained in salt'. They help ego forces to penetrate deeper into matter, thus firing the metabolism and rousing the sphere of the will to sharper consciousness. This is a first step in the direction man is now being challenged to take: that of vitalizing thinking with the will's energy, and thus beginning to partake freely of the wisdom inherent in universal thoughts.

Need we say that it is pointless to approach herbs and spices from the calory-counting angle? That their value lies in imponderable but nonetheless real contributions? Perhaps we might say that they represent the spirit in our foods, for they are the ordering agent that unifies the various taste-components and brings out their individual character. Foods and flavouring belong together, for which reason herbs and spices should be put in the kitchen rather than just on the dining table. Sometimes a person may like to add a touch of this or that, but on the whole the mingling of food and seasoning should start on the stove. A cultivated taste takes offence at flavourings that have not been fully harmonized and related.

A study of the physiology of taste indicates that taste sensations are localized along the edge of the tongue, from tip to root. Perception of the various tastes is arranged as though in a scale that begins at the tongue-tip. Thus we find the two poles 'sweet' and 'bitter' at tip and root respectively, with the qualities 'oily', 'sour', 'biting', 'sharp', 'astringent', and 'salty' between them in that order (cf. Dieffenbach). This gives us a sevenfold taste spectrum, into which the various flavouring agents naturally fit.

> Sweet: Honey, sugar, ripe fruit
> Oily: Nuts, olives, almonds
> Sour: Unripened fruit, capers, lemons, vinegar, sour-grass
> Sharp: Pepper, paprika, leeks and onions, horseradish, mustard
> Astringent: Parsley, marjoram, sage, thyme, rosemary
> Salty: Salt, caraway, summer savoury, lovage
> Bitter: Cinnamon, wormwood, gentian root, etc.

A glance at this spectrum suggests how naturally it fits the threefold plant organism. Sweetness, oiliness, sourness and sharpness are of the fruit and blossom area, astringency of the leaf, the salty and the bitter of rind and root. There are exceptions of course. Sometimes a plant shifts a process that normally belongs in the blossom area to the root, or vice versa. Such plants have therapeutic or other special properties, like sharp-tasting roots or bitter fruits.

Beginning with Hippocrates and up to the time of Paracelsus, the four types of fluids found in the human organism were known to medicine as 'the four humours'. These were black and yellow gall, mucus and blood. The ancient view referred to also connected these basic fluids with the four temperaments, seeing certain characteristics linked with the predominance of one of the four. The temperament one had (the 'earthy' or heavy, the 'watery', or sluggish, the 'airy' – light, or the 'fiery', as Aristotle characterized them) was thought to depend on the particular way these fluids were blended in a person's body. Black gall was said to have earthy darkness and gravity working in it, making for a melancholic temperament. Mucus was connected with water and phlegmatic tendencies, yellow gall with fire and choler, and blood with the fleeting lightness of both air and sanguine natures. Modern spiritual science also sees the four parts of the human entelechy as related to the temperaments. This leads to a rational therapy, aimed at correcting temperamental imbalance with the proper diet.

Melancholics do well to relieve their body-bound heaviness of soul with the choleric spices: pepper, paprika, curry, mustard and the various radishes. That there is a strong modern need for such a therapy is borne out by the fact that in Germany alone forty million pounds of mustard are consumed per year, or about one pound, three ounces to a person. Hot-blooded cholerics should, however, avoid hot sauces and turn instead to seasonings of a more melancholic trend. They need solid, formative, mineralizing root forces to tame the sulphur forces that rule their metabolisms. Bitter or salty roots and bark just fill the bill. Phlegmatic persons on the other hand, are too much involved in their own biological processes (i.e., their life-bodies). It is good for them to let the sanguine seasonings lend them wings, or the choleric ones rouse them. Onions, chives and the umbelliferae should be included in their diet, along with flavourings in the sharp category. The sanguine tendency to be emotionally scattered and torn in all directions needs such phlegmatic foods as nuts, olives, and almonds. And the herb lovage has a calming and settling effect. A vegetable diet is always helpful too in holding the sanguine metabolism to concentrated effort, which in turn means better mental concentration.

It is particularly important to realize what can be done with herbs and spices in times of famine, when quality has to make up for quantity. Seasonings activate the whole organism. They aid assimilation and transubstantiation processes, for they heighten the liveliness of the digestive functions and thus help the user get more nutrients out of his food.

More than this, however, a knowledge of the qualities to be found in herbs and spices makes it possible to influence the building of human tissue by stimulating heart, liver, lungs and kidneys, the four systems that play a rôle in forming protein. Their connection with the various parts of the human entelechy was described in an earlier chapter. Flavourings play right into their harmonious functioning.

In illustration, let us take a look at what modern physiology calls digestive leucocytosis. It has been found that the white blood cells, or leucocytes, multiply after eating. These leucocytes were first thought to be the body's defence against the foreign matter that the food represented. More recent studies show, however, that leucocytosis sets in long before there could be any question of nutrients entering the blood stream. Indeed, the white blood cell count increases even before we start a meal. This can only mean that appetite produces leucocytes. Since appetite is clearly of the soul, or psyche, white blood cells must be the soul's physiological expression, and a rise in their number an indication of soul activity in the metabolic area that belongs to the soul. Red blood cells are similarly to be regarded as the physiological expression of the human ego, lymphocytes of the life body. All these functions take place in the coagulative blood serum, the physiological expression of the physical body. It must be left to biologists of a future time to discover the subtler means needed to prove these facts and arrive at a much fuller understanding of what has been indicated here about the blood. The effect of seasoning agents on the various parts of the entelechy and on the temperaments and organ systems will certainly be made a branch of that research.

Physical body	melancholic	serum	earth	lungs
Life body	phlegmatic	lymphocytes	water	liver
Soul body	sanguine	leucocytes	air	kidneys
Ego	choleric	erythrocytes	fire	heart

CHAPTER SEVENTEEN

Stimulants

COFFEE, TEA, COCOA, TOBACCO AND ALCOHOL

All the so-called stimulants are actually mild poisons. And it is just their poisonous effect that enables partakers to have experiences that they could not otherwise have had, or could have achieved only by considerable effort of the mind and will. The reason for this is that stimulants all affect the body's connection with the soul and spirit. The heightening or other change of consciousness that follows is experienced as pleasure or satisfaction. Stimulants are therefore crutches, but crutches that have greatly endeared themselves to modern man. Strong souls really do not need them. People used to say that culture could be measured by the amount of soap used. Nowadays the amount of stimulants in use gives us the opposite kind of index. The evils of civizliation have caused such spiritual damage that there is a need for the support of stimulants. Goethe said, 'Genius never smokes.' But the average man certainly feels that stimulants, if not used in excess, give him greater energy and social ease.

Except for alcohol, the poisons present in stimulants all derive from plants and are alkaloids (caffeine, theine, theobromine, nicotine). These were described at length in *The Nature of Substance*. They are produced by the cosmic soul element penetrating too deeply into the plant organism. Plants are not organized around a soul, as animals are, and the animal or soul element therefore produces a distorted protein in them. Nitrogen, which we described as the soul-carrier, is the protein component which makes it possible for animals to move their bodies and calls forth sensation and a healthy life of instinct on the soul plane. These reactions, which are normal, healthy ones in animals, do not belong in the plant kingdom. This turns the soul-carrying protein element in poisonous plants into alkaloids. When these nitrogenous poisons are introduced into the human body, their chief influence is on the configuration of the soul, in the sense that they tend to derange the normal adjustment of the soul-spirit to the body. The pricks this gives to the consciousness are relatively harmless if indulgence is not excessive and habitual, but if it is, organic damage can result.

It is an interesting fact that most of the stimulants we use in Europe pour in from other parts of the world: coffee and tea from the Orient (Asia Minor and East Asia), cocoa from the South (Africa), tobacco from the West (America). Europe is responsible only for alcohol. The geographic origin of the stimulants named gives us an index to the nature of the poison they contain.

Coffee is probably the most widely used of stimulants. Germans consume 2·1 kg. (approximately 4½ pounds) per person annually. It is prepared in a variety of ways, ranging from the concentrated Arabian mocha, which is boiled with the sugar already in it and makes a drink that really sharpens consciousness, to the weak potion that can be drunk by the quart.

What effect does coffee have on the human organism, from the spiritual-scientific standpoint?

Rudolf Steiner has described how coffee drinking loosens the life body slightly from the physical, but in a way that still permits the physical to be felt as a solid footing. Coffee makes us more aware of our bodily structure. And since this structure is so wise and logical, our thoughts become logical in their awareness of it. Coffee thus helps thinking to find a firm foundation. The connection between bodily being and thinking keeps calling itself to our attention. Coffee has the same effect on digestion that thought has on our upper man, i.e., a properly ordered metabolism goes hand in hand with orderly thinking. Both are founded on a properly ordered physical structure.

As we have already mentioned, coffee is a plant that has taken up more of the soul element than is right for plants. This gives it its influence on the human soul, whose functions it takes over when it strengthens logic and coherence. This means giving continuity to the thought process. There is danger of this being carried to an extreme in the tendency to get too caught up in a certain thought or theme, which is then done to death. This is particularly true of pedantic and over-thorough people. Newspapers would have many an empty page if there were no coffee for its writers. Rudolf Steiner jokingly called coffee 'the drink of men of letters'. On the other hand, coffee can help correct a tendency to lose the thread and stray off into inconsequential matters. But those who want to make logic their own personal possession must avoid taking coffee and letting it do their thinking for them.

Tea causes a similar loosening of the life body from the physical. In this case, however, the physical body is not felt to be a solid footing. Instead, one has the opposite experience of feeling its wise structure out of reach and deserted while the life body's fluctuating tides take over and influence one's thought life. Thoughts become harder to hold together and cannot attach themselves so easily to facts. Fantasy is stimulated to the point of seeming brilliance that can as readily degenerate into a mere display of mental fireworks.

Tea drinking makes thought witty, light and scintillating. These qualities are typical of a certain phenomenon of our time, and we can easily see why tea has been dubbed 'the drink of diplomats'.

There is a third, plainer partner of these more fashionable beverages: the philistine cocoa. It occupies a place somewhere between tea and coffee, for it too tends to loosen the life body from the physical. The ensuing reaction however, is neither one of sympathetic backward glances nor an antipathetic turning away, but more one of feeling its heaviness. In Europe chocolate is the favoured drink for family parties, weighted down as they are with tradition and conventionality. It conveys a sense of healthy, well-fed satisfaction, of being sheltered within a structure of inherited customs. We must admit though, that chocolate is very nourishing, for it contains fifty percent fat, besides proteins and carbohydrates, and is therefore better for the whole man than the other beverages, as Rudolf Steiner pointed out.

Tobacco is not quite such a harmless kind of indulgence. Kollath groups it with depressants rather than with stimulants. According to statistics, two-hundred and eighty-eight deaths were caused by nicotine in Germany from 1930 to 1934. What makes people want to use such a dangerous poison?

Let us study the occasional smoker (chain smokers are something else again). He usually lights a cigarette when he is in a group but would like to withdraw. It may be a meeting where he fears being taken to task, a conference where he doesn't feel inclined to expose his inmost thoughts, or one of those occasions when life has brought some kind of shock. The smoker envelops himself in a cloud of smoke with the feeling that he can hide there and protect himself. He dons a smoke mantle inside which he can pursue his private thoughts and interests.

Just the opposite can also happen. We may see a very angry man reaching for a smoke in a fit of rage. In cases like these, tobacco seems to calm the upset psyche by keeping the rage from bursting through the enclosing smoke; the angry man regains his composure more quickly, thus enwrapped. Smoking definitely throttles down the desire life. The tobacco smoked by Indians in their peace pipes is said by authorities to have been the real means of enabling them to bury the hatchet.

With those who smoke to excess, there is a heightened danger of isolating oneself to the point where all sensitive feeling for the surrounding world is lost. This makes smoking a social question in a broader sense. Smokers not only fail to notice how they torment non-smokers by poisoning the common indoor air: they do themselves the greatest harm as well, for tobacco can have very dangerous effects long before acute nicotine poisoning sets in. Spiritual science describes nicotine as attacking the rhythmic system. Pulse and breathing get out of tune with each other, and an irregular heart-beat indicates that nerve-sense processes in the upper man are no longer in balance with the metabolic functions of the lower. The blood needs more oyxgen than breathing supplies. This gives rise to a shortness of breath that is unconsciously alarming. The danger lies in the fear thus aroused remaining entirely unconscious, uninfluenced and uncorrected by the head. Chain smokers' hearts revolt in unconscious anxiety. It is shocking to witness the panic heavy smokers feel when cigarettes are in short supply, and they stand lined up for hours, or even days, in front of shops, as they did in war-time. Overindulgence eventually leads to hypertrophy of the heart muscle, kidney malfunction and dropsy, according to Rudolf Steiner. Heart disturbances are caused by the blood being whipped up to a speed faster than the breath can take. This points to a cleavage in the soul-body which underlies all rhythmic functions. Since breathing, which is the seat of social feeling, cannot keep up with an over-accelerated circulation, damage is certain to ensue to the degree of individual vulnerability. For when the soul-body cannot work normally in the lower part of the organism, very serious damage is done to the cells. In time the whole vegetative nervous system suffers.

The tobacco plant is native to America. Like the potato and belladonna, it is a member of the nightshade family. Its effects are typical of the exaggeration inherent in the forces of the West. Already under cultivation by the Aztecs for use in their religious rites, it cast its shadow on the European settlers. The following table demonstrates the sharp increase in the use of tobacco the further west one goes:

Cigarette sales in 1942

Sweden	232 per person annually
France	248 per person annually
Italy	342 per person annually
Germany	372 per person annually
England	820 per person annually
United States	1,100 per person annually

(from Kollath's Textbook of Hygiene)

Europe in its middle position between Western and Oriental poisons, has contributed its speciality, alcohol.

Alcohol contains neither nitrogen nor distorted proteins. It is a combination of carbon, oxygen and hydrogen, active in ways that make it a most dangerous ego-poison. East and West offer the psyche stimulation and a blunting of one's social sensitivity. Alcohol undermines man's self-mastery.

Grapes came originally from Greece, and it was there that wine first came into general use. In fact, it played a ceremonial rôle in the mysteries of Dionysus, while the Bacchanalian rites carried wine-drinking to an excess for which we no longer understand the reason. But it is apparent that wine had a mission for that period. What sort of mission was this?

If we study the grape perceptively, we will see what a special kind of fruit it is. It produces seeds, but their germinal power is very weak. It seems as though this plant had carried its development beyond the point at which most plants stop. For other plants save some of their strength to make the seed capable of reproducing, whereas grapes pour their all into the berry. This reproductive energy makes its appearance in a changed form after fermentation. Plants are built of carbonic acid that is given shape and durability by carbon. Fermentation is a reversal process, and as such causes the carbonic acid to be rejected. In our discussion of carbohydrate foods, we showed how the ego breaks down plant substances in the metabolism, reverses processes that built the plant, and then uses the product of this work in the human nervous system.

In view of the above, we might quote Rudolf Steiner and put it thus: the high point to which the grape has carried its development is the product of an energy similar in kind to the power of self-mastery with which the ego governs the blood.

Wine's mission in the days of Greece and Rome was, then, that of laying the foundation for a new, down-to-earth, human self-awareness. Until then consciousness had been something held in common by families and clans. A new element had to be introduced to pave the way for ego consciousness.

Wine had the mission of developing this in the sense that it undermined man's earlier clairvoyant wisdom. It bound blood and ego together, so that blood became the organ of ego awakening. Man became bold and self-confident, entirely on his own, with no further dependence on external, clairvoyantly perceived guidance. We would remind our readers here of the rôle wine played in Jewish tradition. The grapes brought by scouts from the promised land of Canaan as symbols of its fruitfulness show how especially important wine was to a people to whom making 'graven images' of their god was expressly forbidden. This means that the old clairvoyant perception of spiritual fact was to be uprooted and destroyed in preparation for developing the brain as the ego's instrument.

The New Testament's first story of a miracle performed by Christ Jesus is that called 'The Marriage at Cana'. Here Christ connects the present with the past by turning water into wine, i.e., changing the cosmic consciousness of early days into a more timely consciousness of selfhood.

Jesus Christ's last act, however, was to hold the Lord's Supper, that is, to establish communion. Wine's ancient mission was accomplished at this moment, for its action was now to be replaced by that springing from the wholly Christianized person, from the higher ego. We may therefore say that to take alcohol now is to produce a counter-ego in oneself. For it has the effect of influencing action that should spring freely from the resolution of the ego: alcohol thinks, feels and acts in the ego's place. A person in this situation lets a purely external, material ego dictate to him. Alcohol prevents his own ego from acting, thus making him its slave.

It will be clear from the above that for a really striving spirit to take alcohol at all is retrogressive. It closes doors he was about to open. For habitual takers there is also a problem of physical undermining. It is only a small step from mental confusion and the unleashing of violent feelings to circulatory disturbances accompanied by exhaustion. And then comes the hangover with the depositing of uric acid in the head that goes with too fast and disordered a circulation. The poisons that should have been excreted in urine and fæces are instead stored up in the brain. And the blood, too, fails to renew itself. A person completely saturated with these poisons has delirium tremens with its hideous visions of snakes and mice and other visualizations of the retained substances. The final phase is that of spinal degeneration and the inability to produce red blood corpuscles.

In addition to all this the sufferer's reproductive glands are affected. This is particularly true of women. Men drinkers wreck their nervous system, women their ovaries, which alcohol burdens with a gravitational drag quite out of place there. Rudolf Steiner says that the soul and spirit of a child seeking to make connection with such an ovum at conception, cannot incarnate properly, and is thus condemned to live out its life on earth as an idiot.

Kollath reports that there are about three hundred thousand alcoholics requiring treatment in Germany at the present time. Prior to 1914, one and a half million hectares (approximately three and a half million acres) of land were in alcohol-producing crops in various parts of the globe. But nutritionists with a caloric bias calculated that alcohol contains a not inconsiderable number of calories, and of course producers of alcohol were not slow to turn this 'scientific finding' to account by putting up signs on which one can read how many calories liquor has compared to bread and other staple foods.

The grape is another of those plants now suffering a decline, as can be noted in the many pests and diseases that afflict it.

We state again that we are not in the least interested in making propaganda for or against the stimulants described above. Our purpose is solely to characterize foods and stimulants in a way that includes the findings of spiritual science, leaving the reader free to form his own opinion on the basis of the facts.

CHAPTER EIGHTEEN

The Vitamins

Ever since Pettenkofer founded the caloric theory of nutrition, its inadequacies as a basis for judging food values have become increasingly apparent. It could not help determine the value of salt, for example, though everybody knows that salt is essential to maintaining life. The same could be said of seasonings. And now the discovery of vitamins has really knocked all older concepts out of the running. Nutritionists are beginning to realize, however gradually, that quality simply is more important than quantity.

A hundred years ago, when great advances in physics and chemistry had swept mechanistic concepts into the field of physiology as well, people began to picture the human organism as a thermo-dynamic engine with food as its fuel. The calory, which is equivalent to a certain amount of heat, became the measuring stick for determining the value of a given food.

The Basel physiologist Bunge and his disciples conducted an experiment that cut away the ground from under the caloric point of view. He fed one group of animals fresh milk and another group equal amounts of a synthetic product consisting of a mixture of proteins, fats, salts and sugar all derived from milk. According to the prevailing view, which maintained that the energy and nutritive values of these diets were identical, both should have thrived. But the opposite was true: the animals fed on fresh milk stayed healthy while those fed the synthetic milk died off.

At that period – the last third of the nineteenth century – it was quite impossible to advance any other explanation than that there must be some substance in fresh milk that had escaped analysis. This hypothetical substance was later given the name 'vitamin' because it was so vital to maintaining life. It is still almost as impossible as it was then for orthodox science to conceive vitamins as the life forces of living organisms rather than as material substances.

At any rate, a great wave of research was given to the nature of the vitamin. Scientists discovered that there were such things as vitamin deficiencies, caused by a lack of certain dietary elements. They came to know the various deficiencies and called them A, B, C and D, from which the vitamins that cured them got their names. Later research discovered still other vitamins. An army of researchers took this province for their study. Fact piled on fact till there was a mountain of them, but the basic key remained hidden. Today we list vitamins E, F, G, H, I, K, P and others, though the more perceptive students say that they are all simply aspects of the original A, B, C and D.

But despite the researcher's intelligence and zeal, the inquiry into the real nature of vitamins produced no certainties. Men of stature in the field would spend years of hard careful work producing some extract by fractionization – an extract which, in its 'pure' form, seemed to have especially strong vitamin qualities, only to find that their concentrate could be broken down into substances of completely different chemical structure. There was a case that attracted much attention in 1932-33. O. Rygh, who was trying to isolate the anti-scorbutic Vitamin C, happened on a substance which he identified as methyl-nornarcotine. At exactly the same moment Szent-György turned up with ascorbic acid and called this Vitamin C. Time and again, two research workers hunting for the same vitamin hit upon totally different substances. Vitamins simply eluded capture by chemical analysis. Reading the extensive literature, one is forced to the conclusion that a vitamin is an entity of a higher order. The synthetic products now on the market may perhaps be carriers of vitamin action, but they cannot always be counted on for effectiveness.

A picture may serve to clarify this statement. A gramophone record can be made of various materials. The important thing about records is not their composition, but the music recorded on them, which they reproduce. It would seem that the chemical structure of a vitamin is of far less account than the energy that forms and uses the substance.

What are the characteristics of Vitamins A, B, C and D?

A quantitative method of vitamin determination was hit upon when, in experiments with deficiency diseases in animals, comparative measurement was made of the time it took animals to recover on this or that feed. Four kinds of vitamin entities were distinguished. The results were carefully tabulated by H. Schall, and one can see from a study of his tables what amount of a given vitamin is present in a given food.

It is not possible to judge human reactions accurately by those of animals. Nevertheless, this method of determination has a far firmer basis in reality than the volumetric standards of the chemists, according to which one needs so and so many milligrams of ascorbic acid or carotine.

The following table, which shows vitamin qualities and quantities of various foods measured in units, is extremely interesting in what it reveals:

		Vitamin A	B	C	D
Seed	Grain	1	–	2	–
Fruit	Seed Fruit (apple)	2	2	1	–
	Stone Fruit (plum)	3	1	2	–
	Berries (bilberries)	4	2	1	–
Green Vegetables	Leaves (spinach)	3	4	2	–
	Stems (chard)	1	2	2	–
	Stem and bulb (kohlrabi)	–	3	2	–
Root		2	2	3	3

We see from the above that Vitamin A occurs in those parts of plants where warmth is the predominant dynamic, i.e., where seeds and fruit ripen in hot summer sunshine. Vitamins B and C, on the other hand, occur where light and chemism, the starch-forming forces of assimilation, predominate and bring forth an abundance of green foliage. And in the root, where densification processes are localized, we find Vitamin D. This already gives us a clue to what vitamins are, and the facts become increasingly obvious when we follow it up with a study of the basic phenomena of the deficiency diseases.

The best way to do this is to paint in bold strokes the essential features of the various avitaminoses as Goethe would have done, and at the same time note what substances are natural vitamin-carriers, and what their relationship is to the living whole of nature. For we will never get to the facts by studying each vitamin singly. To do that, we must look at the total picture with an eye for the way nature's basic processes interweave.

A start was made with this sort of study in *The Nature of Substance*. We will therefore restrict ourselves here to a brief resumé.

It has been shown that Vitamin A occurs in oils, fat, fruits and blossoms. Butter is especially rich in it. All these substances are closely related to the warmth element. Blossoms, fruits and seed-borne oils are products of the hottest months. Oils burn, revealing the fire-force latent in them. One is really justified in calling them a condensation of universal fire. Animal fats and oils express the same basic character on their own level. Whales, seals and other Arctic mammals have a coat of blubber that regulates their warmth organisms.

What, then, is warmth's real nature?

It can be seen in its most classic form in the way plants expand into the upper atmosphere under the influence of warmth. They are carried up and out into the warmth cosmos on wings of hydrogen. This primal phenomenon can be witnessed in every process of a physical nature. Whatever is subjected to warmth expands. Warmth is the expanding, unfolding growth element.

Stunting is one of the outstanding symptoms of the deficiency disease caused by a lack of Vitamin A. This is accompanied by other disturbances in the organism, particularly in the sense organs (the eyes), in the peripheral, epithelian cells. But dwarfing is the most conspicuous development.

This seems the place to remind readers that the size of a creature reveals something of its relationship to the cosmos. Rudolf Steiner indicated that man's size is not relative, but absolute, set by the cosmos. His spiritual entelechy and the ego forces, which are his human form's top architects, are at home in warmth. Disturbing his warmth forces therefore always upsets the connection between his body and the spiritual core of his being that governs both soul and bodily processes.

Thus it is clear that insufficient stimulation by the fire forces latent in oils, fat, blossom elements, fruit and seeds leads to a decreased development of inner warmth and affects growth adversely. The peripheral parts of the organism are obviously going to be the worst deprived. The skin and its adjuncts are therefore the first to show morbid changes. But an organism so basically undermined cannot provide the right sort of home for an indwelling spirit in any of its parts.

It seems fair to say that though Vitamin A links up with a substance or substances that give it a footing, it is not itself a material entity, but rather living, creative warmth that makes for itself a physical counterpart in fruits and blossoms, seeds, fats and oils.

Green plants are Vitamin C producers. It is in their green foliage that photosynthesis takes place. The form and substance of each single leaf is of light's shaping and organizing. In an earlier chapter we called the virginal starch created in leaves an enchanted rainbow, which shines forth again when the plant develops coloured blossom in its upward growth. Here we see before our very eyes the metamorphoses light undergoes, from its descent into matter through assimilation, to its radiant re-emergence in the stars of blossoms.

Green leaves, then, are latent light. The avitaminosis caused by an insufficiency of green leafy vegetables is known as scurvy. Sufferers from this disease look as though they had been shut away from light. One has only to observe plants grown in darkness to see how important light is to everything organic. The more highly organized a creature is, the more complex is the rôle light plays. But readers will remember how often we have pointed out that higher species have inherent powers radiating from an inner centre as a result of light's having been interiorized in them. This light process starts with gastrulation, which marks the moment when the exterior is involuted and becomes the interior. Thus a living light process inside man opposes the light of the cosmos round about him.

Man's skin surface is the place where inner and outer light must be brought into balance. In healthy individuals this regulating takes care of itself. Healthy inner light activity is evidenced in a clear, smooth skin and rosy cheeks. When external light gets the upper hand, the organism protects itself by making the skin brown. This can be due either to external sunlight or to a slackening of inner light. In the latter case, the sick person gives the impression of a wilted plant. Scurvy patients have the yellowish-brown skin colour mentioned, and as the illness progresses their skins begin to break down and bleed. Other organs involved in the human organism's light processes, such as the kidneys and the suprarenal glands, also deteriorate.

We repeat that neither narcotine nor ascorbic acid are themselves Vitamin C. This vitamin is living light that has become latent in green foliage. A lack of it in the human diet means insufficient stimulation of man's power to develop inner light. And just as warmth is the medium for the human spirit that has formed man's body, light is the element in which the soul works and has its being. The soul lacks a firm foothold in persons whose light organism is out of sorts.

Vitamin B has been found to occur in the skins and husks of fruit and seeds, particularly the cereal grains, with rice at the very top of the list.

Rice is the staple food of East Asia. Indeed, a large percentage of its population eats nothing but rice. This caused no illness in the days when rice was eaten just as it came from the rice field. But as Asia began to feel the impact of European ways, rice was subjected to milling and hulling, and the natives could get only polished rice. This gave rise to beri-beri, the cause of which was at first a mystery. For a while it was thought to be the plague or some other kind of epidemic. Chance brought the solution to a Dutch doctor. It was his task to care for beri-beri patients in a hospital. He had a poultry farm, where he fed the chickens polished rice. It was not long before he observed that his hens were ill, with symptoms very much like those of his beri-beri patients. Things went from bad to worse until one day a shortage of polished rice made it necessary to feed his hens rice polishings. The chickens recovered immediately. Rice-bran extract was then tried in hospitals, with the result that beri-beri came to be recognized as a deficiency disease.

Obviously, husks must contain a force of some kind. To help to visualize it, imagine formless space extending in every direction, and then a circling gesture shaping this chaos into a sphere and thus ordering it.

All myths of creation suggest such a gesture. God first created the heavens and the earth. Shaping heaven's vault would be much the same, only on an infinite scale, as shaping a small, finite globe. The ancients called the starry order set in cosmic space 'the music of the spheres'. The music we know on earth is a reflection of it. And if we explore the effect of universal harmonies on matter in its subtlest aspects, we will see that they are an ordering energy, which we have termed chemism. I showed in *The Nature of Substance* that the starry order, tone and chemistry are the product of identical or very similar laws, of one and the same universal ordering element, and that its primal phenomenon is the rim or sheath of the universe. Sheath-giving forces are ordering forces. There have to be enclosing bounds from which to reflect and radiate back into an interior. This means giving space order from outside. A deficiency of Vitamin B means that the organism lacks the proper physical foundation for these chemical life-processes.

When these elements are missing in a person's diet, his basic chemistry, or ordering capacity, is insufficiently stimulated. Beri-beri has all the symptoms of this lack. The ankle muscles lose their capacity to contract, and examination shows that it no longer has its normal order or structure. Muscle fibres dissolve or separate. Paralysis sets in, and the nerves start to degenerate.

We must emphasize again that Vitamin B is not synonymous with this or that chemical. It is an ordering force located in the periphery or sheath of things; it is chemism, creating order within organisms.

Vitamin D is said to be present in fish liver oils, and phosphorus and sea-salt are both carriers. It would be hard to understand why liver oil carries this vitamin if it were not for the fact that cholesterines formed in the liver are found in it as liquids. These substances are known to be structural material for the whole organism. Supportive tissue and cell membranes are both made of it.

All these cholesterines and lipoids contain phosphorus, and it is characteristic of phosphorus to enhance densifying, mineralizing tendencies. We see just how skeletons are made when we watch salt crystallize out of a solution. Man's bony structure literally 'crystallizes out' of the fluid embryo.

When there is not enough of this Vitamin D stimulation in a person's diet, his basic formative forces lack support and he cannot build up a proper bony system. The consequence is a deficiency disease known as rachitis.

We reiterate: Vitamin D is not just some chemical substance or other, but cosmic formative energy seen primally active in salt crystallization. A person whose system lacks it cannot build up a mineralized physical image of his being.

	Being	*Carrier*	*Deficiency symptom*
Vitamin A	Warmth	Oils (seeds)	Stunted growth
Vitamin B	Order	Husks	Beri-beri
Vitamin C	Light	Green plants	Scurvy
Vitamin D	Form	Lipoids	Rachitis

The table above recalls another where we showed hydrogen, nitrogen, oxygen and carbon related to the four Aristotelian elements. Earth, water, air and fire are indeed synonymous with shape, order (chemism), light and warmth in their finer elements. And we came to know the four food categories, the four cereal species, to mention just a few of the various things we have shown to be related to man's fourfold entelechy. The basic phenomena appear again and again in the lesser phenomena of these neverending metamorphoses.

Summing up, we may term vitamins 'currents of energy' not yet fixed and substantial, which co-operate in the making of complete, healthy protein. In spiritual science these energies are known as etheric formative forces. They are not to be confused with the hypothetical ether of the physicists, however, but rather looked upon as the lowest level of non-physical reality.

The experiments on which our conclusions are based were reported in fullest detail in *The Nature of Substance*. They enabled the writer to demonstrate the effect of the four basic cosmic forces on various living test-materials. He was concerned not only with questions of their effect on organisms, but with demonstrating their existence as cosmic qualities.

Werner Kollath has done some interesting research work that indicates the existence of food values, which he calls 'auxones'. Animal-feeding experiments that included them, whether in combination with vitamins or not, had noteworthy results. They seem to be growth-inducers similar to vitamins. We will not go wrong in regarding them as variations and metamorphoses of the living formative forces that make and maintain living organisms. For one thing has certainly come out clearly: that the four Vitamins A, B, C and D are simply basic types, capable of as many mutations as the world of plants.

CHAPTER NINETEEN

The Plant in the Light of Modern Agricultural Chemistry

If people are to be given a really healthy and nourishing vegetable diet, we will have to lay a basis for it in the way food plants are produced. A close look at modern agriculture can prove quite a shock, so far from nature has it moved.

In the last century, Liebig, Woehler and Pettenkofer began researches approaching the realm of life with the selfsame concepts that had led to such progress in the physical sciences, sciences concerned only with lifeless minerals. Woehler himself said that the discovery of a way to synthesize uric acid gave the *coup de grâce* to the vague life-force science had hitherto supposed to exist. This was the moment when agricultural science too came under the sway of a physical-chemical way of thinking. An agricultural chemistry was developed which taught that plants absorb from the soil certain mineral substances, called essential nutrients. Crops rob the soil of these elements, and if the land is to go on producing they must be replaced. Liebig evolved his NPK formula for a balanced soil, thereby earning the title 'father of artificial fertilizing'.

Logical though this approach seems, a thorough study of artificial fertilization methods casts many a grave doubt on its validity.

Mineral fertilizers do increase crop yields at the beginning. But their use for only a matter of decades has produced phenomena that should give us pause – especially considering how short a time-span these decades represent measured against the many centuries our soils have been under cultivation. We have only to observe what has happened to the quality and health of plants forced by these methods, as shown in their vulnerability to disease and parasites, new species of which keep developing. It is noteworthy that the pesticide industry has grown in almost exact proportion to the growth of the chemical fertilizer industry.

Agriculture has become industrialized, undermining that instinctive farming technique on which the future too will have to depend to some extent for wholesome food. Nowadays many farmers have become food manufacturers.

This development is the outcome of a tragic error. Plants are living organisms and cannot be approached with the mechanical concepts of the NPK-balance theory. It is simply not true that the plant absorbs nutrients from the soil alone: it is an entity built up by the entire universe. Life laughs at the law of the conservation of matter. There is no such thing as a 'balance of substances' to be found anywhere in its realm. I devoted some space in *The Nature of Substance* and in preceding chapters of this book to explaining that matter is merely a fixed earthly stage in macrocosmic processes. Goethe said that 'Heavenly forces ascend and descend, passing golden chalices from hand to hand'. This is a marvellous fact of living organisms that can be understood and scientifically proven. Matter is capable of radical change in its ascending and descending, ranging from the stage of pure, macrocosmic process to the densest of substances that can be weighed and chemically analysed. The minerals from which plants are formed derive originally from cosmic space where the being of the plant belongs in the interplay of earth and cosmos. These minerals show up in plant residues at the final stage of the life process and are absorbed into the earth as an inheritance from the vegetable kingdom. We see the profound truth of the saying, 'It is not the soil that produces plants, but rather plants the soil.'

Baron Albrecht von Herzeele, the man who wrote these words, was a nineteenth-century researcher. He published writings on the vegetable origin of inorganic substances around 1879. He proved that the ash content of plants grown in distilled water changes. Further series of experiments indicated that a wonderful alchemy within living plants actually changes one mineral substance into another. He performed about five hundred analyses, proving that carbonic acid can change into magnesium, the latter into calcium, and calcium in turn into sulphur by way of phosphorus. In other experiments, nitrogen was changed into potash:

$$CO_2 \rightarrow Mg \rightarrow Ca \rightarrow P \rightarrow S$$
$$N \rightarrow K$$

Plants, then, can transmute one substance into another. Herzeele comments that this is an every-day occurrence in the organic realm, since it is the nature of life to create substances in the first place and then to change them into something else inside living organisms. 'Living things die, but dead elements are by-products, not intentional creations.' Nature has not created calcium, magnesium, phosphorus and potash and then made plants out of them, as though in a chemical laboratory. It has been able to create plants because a creative archetype of each such organism pre-existed. The various components were then drawn into this living idea and made to coalesce. The basic elements described by present-day chemistry are not primary substances, and the moment we begin to realize that they are in a constant flux of becoming and change, they cease to seem at all basic or simple, as Herzeele observes. Unfortunately no attention was paid to his comprehensive findings in all the furore over advances in the fields of physics and chemistry. No matter how hard it is to see merit in something that contradicts habits of thought and previous assumptions, Herzeele should have been given a chance to be heard and his findings checked. The trouble was then, as it still is now, that what could not be understood tended to be ignored, for, as the saying goes, 'what oughtn't to be true cannot be'.

Research carried on for decades by the present writer fully confirmed Herzeele's findings and added to them. In *The Nature of Substance* I described in detail the changes in weight observed in seedlings grown in sealed jars. These changes corresponded to rhythmic processes in the universe, showing that the coming into being and subsequent disappearance of matter in an organism is part of a universal pattern. Moon rhythms were found to have a special influence on relationships between substances.

The curves reproduced here indicate that the waxing moon favours the generation of material substances, the waning moon their dissolution – a fact that shows why Rudolf Steiner advised farmers to sow seed, apart from legumes, on the waxing moon (Fig. 12).

The author's research was done with cress seeds as material. When the jars were opened during waning-moon periods, a very sharp aroma escaped from them. This was only natural, for the disappearance of matter always means that it is

WEIGHING EXPERIMENTS · 1934

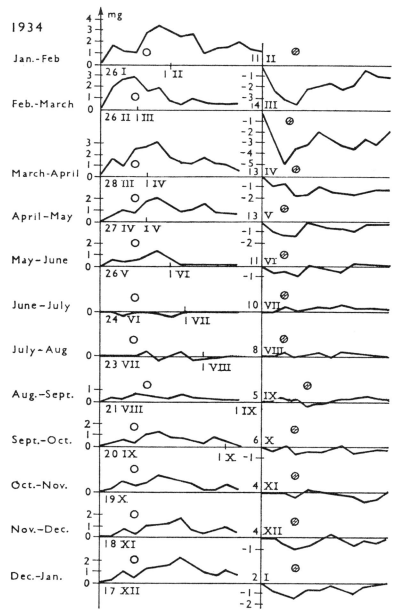

Fig. 12
The rising and declining of matter according to the lunar cycle.

being breathed out into the universe, thus enhancing the scent element. Experiments done on radishes growing in the open confirmed the above findings, in that those sown at the full moon were bigger and heavier, whereas those sown on the waning moon did not grow as large, but instead developed sharper aroma.

The author's findings were confirmed by the French scholar, H. Spindler. Two articles by him were published in the *Bulletin du Laboratoire Maritime de Dinard* in 1946 and 1948, recording increases and decreases of matter in algae. He combined these studies with observations of changes in iodine and potash content. The fact that iodine increased in sealed-up algae contrary to all expectation and later declined again made Spindler speak of a form of iodine 'not as yet subject to material fixity'. He states: 'J'affirme que le monde vivant, organique n'a pas pris son appui sur le monde inorganique qui l'aurait précédé – c'est au contraire la croûte minérale, qui a été élaborée par la terre primordiale un peu comme l'écorce est produit par l'arbre vivant.'

It can be gathered from the above that present-day agricultural chemistry is based on completely mistaken assumptions. It should recognize the fact that plants are living organisms which find a suitable anchor-hold in the soil, and that this soil must be prepared in a way that enables plants to take up the cosmic influences necessary to their growth.

From time immemorial, farmers have believed that it was humus that made their fields and garden fertile. Now, since Liebig, they look to potash, nitrogen and phosphorus. The old-timers were right; they still had a feeling for what life is.

It is obvious that plants take up elements present in the soil. But this is not the sole determining factor. Moreover, they are able to absorb soil nutrients only because the soil was made by plants originally. That is why composting is one of the most essential farming practices. The important thing is not so much what materials are composted as the fact that plant wastes are reduced to the ultimate stage of disintegration, so that soil thus prepared takes a fresh start and becomes a suitable matrix for new growth.

To do this properly means 'putting heart' into the compost heap by encouraging the presence of all sorts of living elements and creatures from bacteria to earthworms. The latter play the most important part, for they eat rotted stuff and earth along with it. These get mixed with glandular secretions as they are digested and come out as the little mounds of droppings we see on the ground. They are so fine and so perfectly mixed as to make the most wonderful earth for plants to grow in. A soil worked by all these little creatures is really seasoned.

In his course for farmers, Rudolf Steiner gave much valuable advice on developing a really healthy agriculture. The methods it gave rise to are known as 'bio-dynamic'. The course devoted considerable attention not only to proper composting, but to questions of using manures to best advantage and basing field management on keeping cattle. For it was pointed out that farms, being alive, must be kept in balance as living organisms and become self-sustaining, supplying their own manure.

When the above methods have really caught on, it will be possible to feed people decent, healthy, nourishing food again, instead of the blown-up overgrown produce seen in modern markets. And it will be possible to remedy the eroded condition now threatening the soil that bids fair to make a spreading desert bearing witness to our sins against nature. The cutting down of woods and hedgerows, the unnatural regulation of rivers and the mineralization for which an agriculture that has become an industry is responsible, all contribute to making the earth's surface ever less fertile. An ominous sign of it is the lowering of the water table.

Things are bound to keep on going downhill until we have stopped applying to the living kingdoms the measuring, weighing and counting that properly belong only in technology. Mistakes tend to end up as catastrophes. But the immensity of modern error and the tragedy that threatens to follow in its wake are unmatched in history. Misguided production, in agriculture too, makes itself felt over the whole earth nowadays, not just locally. A sick soil can only produce world famine in the years to come.

CHAPTER TWENTY

The Capillary-Dynamic Technique

A few digressing comments at this point will make the following chapters more readily comprehensible. They deal with a technique by means of which life processes are made to reveal themselves in certain patterns.

Perhaps a common childhood experience will help the reader see how this is done. Older people surely remember from their schooldays having a note book ruined by a large blob of ink spilled on it, usually unintentionally. Then frantic, clumsy efforts would be made to undo the mischief with a blotter, which only enlarged the disaster area. The more experienced skilfully shrank the blot by sucking up most of the ink with a corner of their blotters. Then one sat back and observed with artistic pleasure or cold scientific curiosity the pattern thus produced, with special attention to the bizarre and jagged forms that appeared on the edges of the spot.

The behaviour of fluids absorbed by blotting paper or any uncoated paper such as that employed in filters was noted in the 1800's by dyers, who used them for the purpose of separating or determining dye mixtures. The researcher L. Kolisko applied this process to a study of metals and of their connection with various planetary spheres. The title of her published findings was *Star Influences on Earthly Substances*. The author took up her work and made use of the same method in studies of the sap of plants with curative properties, studies conducted in his research laboratory at the Clinical Therapeutic Institute in Arlesheim near Basel.

A basic finding was that mineral solutions produce a more or less linear edge, while plant saps make most lively articulated, multi-formed ones, which we therefore called plant signatures.

The procedure used in these studies was as follows: A specially selected, homogeneous paper was placed in a measured quantity of the test solution, either in strips or rolled into cylinders. Great care was taken to keep meteorological factors such as humidity, temperature and barometric pressure constant. Humidity is obviously especially important. This was controlled by vaporizers or the absorption of too much moisture by calcium chloride. Thus a constant climate was maintained in the research area.

Now one might ask what is happening when plant sap counteracts gravity and climbs up through the fibres of a filter-paper to make a colour pattern typical of that plant. The explanation given by physics, that this is due to capillary attraction, is only partly right, for the patterns vary and are characteristic signatures of each single plant. Other forces must account for this phenomenon, forces that the physico-chemical outlook can no longer grasp.

The plant's life principle is connected with its sap. Here are to be found the cosmic and terrestrial formative forces that project the plant into threefold spatial form and account for the development of the many plant species from one primal form, as diverse as daisies and cabbages. Sap is the carrier of these formative forces. And the plant's dense form is a precipitate of the living being carried by the sap.

When plant sap is extracted, diluted and put in contact with the filter paper, it is set free and can show us in forms and colours something of the living, moving forces present in it. Obviously we will see forms corresponding to the wide variety of plants in nature. It is as though a new plant grows up before our very eyes in the pattern made by the ascending sap.

This new plant is so sensitive to every environmental influence that one feels challenged to experiment. With appropriate mirrors and lenses one can, for example, focus the rays of Venus on the pattern as it grows. Observation shows a definite effect on the pattern.

Why is this?

It can be taken for granted, as long since proven, that sun, moon and stars exercise a very definite influence on plant growth and patterning. I described in *The Nature of Substance* how plants are built up, both as regards qualitative and quantitative aspects, in cosmic sun, moon and star rhythms. It need scarcely surprise us, then, to find Venus affecting the formative forces of the plant thus irradiated and bringing about a metamorphosis of its 'signature'.

Setting up this experiment is such a job, however, that the stars' earthly-material representatives were tried instead of direct star radiation. In *The Nature of Substance* I discussed at some length the fact that copper is actually the materialized light of Venus, silver the moon's light, gold the sun's light. Similarly, lead comes from Saturn, iron from Mars, quicksilver from Mercury, tin from Jupiter. Thus, when a drop of a solution of these metals is added to plant sap, or when a cylinder that has been exposed to plant sap is further exposed to a suitably diluted metal, the plant signature changes and comes to resemble the pattern made by exposure to concentrated starlight. When years of experience have made a person so familiar with these patterns that he can 'read' the writing thus obtained, it is as though he were listening to a conversation between plant and star.

Daily series of experiments were carried out to gain this experience and to study variations in the form-language of the stars. Apple juice was extensively tested in 1929. A certain tree was chosen, and its apples picked and carefully stored in straw. An apple was pressed every day and its juice tested. On the first day of November, two patterns in the series varied so much from the one we had become accustomed to getting that we thought some sort of mistake must have been made. When the series was run through a second time, using fresh solutions of the metal, we got the same result: abnormal gold and silver patterns. The accustomed blossom-like, radiating gold figure had become a cloudy grey confusion. The beautiful silver pattern that had always looked like ears of grain now exhibited club-like bone forms. When we repeated the series at two-hour intervals we continued to get the same results into the afternoon hours. Only when evening came did the pattern clear up at all, and the next morning it was more beautiful than ever.

What had actually happened here?

Since no change of any kind had been made in the laboratory organization and procedure, we had to attribute it to some cosmic disturbance. And a study of astronomical data then revealed the fact that there had actually been an eclipse of the sun on the 1st November. It was not locally visible, but had nevertheless registered itself in the pattern change. Conjunctions of sun and moon so preoccupy the formative forces of both heavenly bodies as to stop their normal irradiation of the earth. Later on, similar phenomena were often observed in characteristic constellations (cf. Figs. 13-16).

Now it might be asked what practical value experiments of this kind had for nutritional research.

Not only is it important in the case of both food plants and those with healing properties to learn something of their connection with the starry universe: one knows and understands them better for having a chance to observe how they come to grips with cosmic forces in their environment. We do not really know a person when we have only seen him in calm and peaceful moments; we have to be able to observe how he meets the problems life brings him.

Metals, then, help make a plant's real nature visible. In its struggle with the metal that has been added to the solution used in the experiments described, we see how weak or strong it is and the degree of its relationship to the various processes represented by the metals.

The following chapter will be devoted to exploring this theme further.

CHAPTER TWENTY-ONE

Preparation

SHOULD FOODS BE EATEN RAW OR COOKED?

It takes a proper understanding of plants and their rhythmic cycles to know whether they should be eaten raw or cooked, and even at what time of day to harvest them.

Plants are like streams in the sense that the life moving through them, like the water in a stream-bed, is constantly changing. In this sense a plant is a vessel into which pour cosmic streams of life. Their nature varies greatly with the time of day. A person who has observed nature at close range knows, for example, that blossoms open at sunrise and close again at sunset. In view of the many experiments already mentioned, where it was demonstrated that the very substance of a plant undergoes rhythmic changes as the hours go by, no one need be surprised to hear that it makes a difference what time of day edible plants are gathered. They are simply not the same thing at night that they were in the morning, and this holds true in comparing them at noon and midnight. The capillary-dynamic method makes it possible to see these differences.

A plant of convolvulus arvensis was selected. At sunrise one of its tendrils, bearing leaves and blossoms, was cut off, together with a portion of the root. These were wrapped in dampened cloths and put in the cellar. At noon and sunset, similar cuttings were made, and at midnight the last remnants of the plant were taken. Then all four cuttings were simultaneously tested by the capillary-dynamic method.

A person sensitive to the language of form could see that the morning picture showed a radiating, upward-climbing tendency, while the evening one made the very opposite gesture, almost as though the plant wanted to go underground. The noon picture, in contrast, seemed to have reached a rather chaotic resting-point, while the midnight one, though very similar, was earthier, more regular, and shadowy.

This indicated that a morning harvesting of vegetables gives consumers the benefit of freeing, sprouting formative forces

active early in the day, whereas an evening harvest yields vegetables in which plastic, shaping elements prevail. Blossoms, fruit
and leafy vegetables, having an affinity to the first category, will
be particularly strong in freeing easing forces if picked early in
the day. This is important in a diet that seeks to develop just such
tendencies. And the plastic, shaping forces inherent in the root
and stalk vegetables are strongest in the late hours of the day.
They can be used to advantage in a diet of root vegetables
designed to control an over-active metabolism. And in the case of
seeds, might we not expect grain cut in the morning to make
especially good bread and grain harvested in the afternoon to
provide a seed-stock with good keeping qualities?

Chaotic forces permeate the whole plant kingdom at noon and
midnight. These are obviously the poorest harvesting periods.
The ancients were perfectly familiar with the Noontide forces,
which they identified with the dreaded 'Noon-witch'; it was not a
pleasant thing for a tired reaper to meet her and give in to her
enticements. And people of modern times still have a feeling that
uncanny forces are abroad at midnight.

As to whether food should be cooked or eaten raw, we might
comment as follows:

The human organism has to come to terms with the substances
from the other kingdoms of nature which man takes in as foods.
That is what digestion really is. It is hardest to come to terms with
minerals, easiest with animal substances, like milk. For in the
latter case, life and soul forces have already worked them over.
This explains why infants can take milk without any difficulty,
but only adults can take sharply seasoned food. It also makes a
difference which part of a plant we eat, whether root, stalk,
leaves, seed or blossom, and whether it is cooked or eaten raw.

Let us see what really happens when a food is cooked. It may
help dispel the increasing fanaticism met with on this question if
it is placed in the large perspective of all-around natural fact.

Let us look again at plants. They are really light beings fettered
to the earth. They span the space between sky and earth (or, as
Goethe would have it, between the poles of light and darkness),
relating to both in never-ending change. With their leaves and
blossoms they reach up into realms of light while anchoring

themselves in darkness with their roots. Goethe shows in his *Theory of Colour* how colours come into being between light and darkness as the result of a struggle between these two poles. Light looked at through darkness makes the warm, bright colours red and yellow. Darkness with light shining into it makes the cold dark colours blue and violet. Combining the polarities by mixing blue and yellow gives us reconciling green. These phenomena are archetypes of many a mysterious fact that exists in nature, including plants. When the latter are related to the rainbow we begin to see what cosmic laws obtain in them. We have already described the process whereby starch is formed in the green leaf and shown in what sense it is to be regarded as an enchanted rainbow become matter.

What happens to starch after this in the living flow of plant growth?

Etherealizing warmth, cosmic ripening forces, lay hold on the plant and etherealize the starch, refine it in the blossom substance, and then sublimate it into sugar as this forms in the nectaries and ripened fruit. Sugar and starch are both carbohydrates and scarcely differ from each other chemically. But we may compare the two and say that sugar is a higher form of carbohydrate that has undergone refinement by cosmic warmth processes.

And there are further phases to this metamorphosis: beyond the sugar stage, blossom colours come into being. The enchanted rainbow announces its presence in reds, yellows, blues and violets. As we walk through meadows full of blossoms we see about us the heaven-born brightness of colour that had been transformed into starches earlier in the season but is now set free again by cosmic fire forces.

And the flowers fade as they pour colour out into the universe. Their fragrance dissipates. Now they begin to fall into dust as their delicate substantiality streams back into the universe where it originated. The balloonist Piccard reports encountering clouds of pollen in the stratosphere striving sunwards. As we see, there are further and further stages of etherealization. The plant's green centre is the starting point, and the sublimation process moves from there upward, passing through ever finer stages until, after a burst of scent and colour, the plant disappears from the scene before us.

But what happens to starch when the opposite pole, earth forces of coldness and contracting gravity, act upon it?

Here we have the origin of sturdy fibres, of solid structure-giving elements in plants. The further down we go toward the root, the firmer and woodier the plant becomes. These substances, called cellulose, are also carbohydrates, but they are more solid and compact than the starches.

Thus we have in plants a threefold nature that submits the roots to earthy densifying processes, while, at the top, it goes on past the blossom stage into complete dematerialization.

These facts lay the groundwork for finding an answer to the question as to how cooking, which simply means bringing heat in the form of steam, hot fat or boiling water into contact with our food affects it. Is it not perfectly obvious that we are doing just what nature does in her dematerializing, ripening, warmth processes? We are simply continuing what she began. But is it good to do this? That is the point.

A further look at the threefold plant in the light of what has just been stated on the subject may help to clarify this issue.

Blossoms are the realm to which the cosmos devotes a maximum of ripening, freeing warmth forces. Where this is carried further, fading, over-ripeness and decay takes place. Therefore, to cook the upper portions of a plant means to carry to a further point a natural process which has already reached the limit of the desirable in nature. This causes such foods to undergo something analogous to fading, or even to dying. Biologists would say that it destroys the vitamins.

This should be kept in mind when it comes to making teas from blossom elements such as chamomile or linden or elder flowers. It is also true of compotes and such delicate blossom or bud vegetables as cauliflower, brussels sprouts and asparagus. Boiling teas made from flowers for even just one or two minutes can convince the reader that every bit of the taste, aroma, and other imponderable qualities are entirely lost; the brew has 'faded' and flattened. It is therefore advisable to let such teas just boil, then let them infuse.

Capillary-dynamic pictures were made to illustrate the laws referred to above. They were most convincing (cf. Figs. 17-20).

An extract of elder blossoms was made with the cold water method for the first test (Fig. 17). In the second test the blossoms were subjected to a five-minute boiling in a reflux condenser. It is marvellous to see how clearly the whole aspect of the blossom strobile is suggested in the first picture, while in the second there is no such thing as structure.

With fruits one finds considerable differences, but on the whole they should be eaten raw when fully ripe. One variation of the cooking process is to wrap blossoms, fruits and aromatic leaves in dough and fry them in deep fat. Some old favourites prepared this way are elder and acacia blossoms and salvia or sage leaves. This method in effect constructs a kind of shell that keeps the essence in the food. Analogous in nature is the seed-forming process, in which an evolutionary dynamic is turned into an involutionary one. That describes perfectly what goes on in the frying pan. A high degree of ripening is achieved, giving foods so prepared the dietetic value and quality of tropical fruits.

What of root vegetables of opposite polarity?

In their case, the earth has kept them isolated from the cooking process involved in exposure to the sun. Thus cooking gives carrots, beets, celeriac and oyster plant what they failed to get in outer nature. It lightens and lifts them as though into the realm of cosmic warmth activity. Pictorially speaking, we bring them up above the ground. And we find that cooking makes them soft, aromatic, even sweet. The capillary-dynamic picture shows that the pattern characteristic of roots changes to a leaf or, in some instances, a blossom form when the juices of these vegetables are cooked (cf. Figs. 19-20).

Housewives can develop a feeling for the special nature of each plant, however. They might, for example, learn to notice that the reddish-yellow colour of a carrot actually signifies that the blossom element has penetrated all the way down into the root, giving it a more delicate shape. In this case less warmth is needed to mellow it than with various other roots. Indeed, it can even be eaten raw on occasion.

Green leaves, as the central part of plants, become ever more blossom-like the higher up the plant they grow, as a result of the heating process in the sun's warmth. Cooking such leafy vegetables as spinach and cabbage has the same effect. Again, these qualitative changes show up clearly in the capillary pictures.

A study of the cabbage family led to a particularly enlightening series of experiments (Figs. 21-25).

Figures 21-23 represent capillary-dynamic patterns obtained in three experiments with cabbage juice. Figure 21 shows the pattern of the uncooked juice, Figure 22 juice cooked for five minutes, and Figure 23 juice cooked for twenty minutes in a reflux condenser. The juice cooked for the shorter time developed much lighter and less compact forms than the uncooked juice; they have something of the flower pattern. Whereas the juice that was cooked for half an hour was 'cooked to death', to the point of losing form. Brief cooking may therefore be said to raise leafy cabbage to the flower level, while prolonged cooking causes what has been described above as the final stage of blossoming: complete disappearance. All that is left to eat is the dead remnant.

If we compare these cabbage juice pictures with those of cauliflower reproduced in Figures 24 and 25, we find a startling similarity between them and the briefly cooked cabbage shown in Figure 22. Indeed, they are almost identical. This indicates that properly prepared cabbage that is not overcooked can be raised in quality to the level of cauliflower.

The picture obtained from cooked cauliflower confirms the fact that blossom elements cannot stand cooking; it is practically identical with that of cooked cabbage juice. Cooks can learn from this not to do more than bring cauliflower just to the boiling point.

We must warn readers that the cooking periods chosen in the case of the above experiments were determined to some extent by the fact that we were dealing with plant juices, not with the whole leaves, heads and buds as in the kitchen. In the latter case, structural matter encloses and protects the juices to a great extent. This makes a difference in the length of cooking. The five minute period may safely be exceeded.

It should be emphasized again, however, that leafy vegetables need only very brief cooking. Ten minutes, which is double the cooking period for juices, is plenty for cabbage, for leaves are not too far removed from blossoms and are therefore quickly lifted to this higher level. A minute or so longer and it is already cooked to death – or, as we might say, has gone past the blossoming stage and faded.

It is also advisable to steam rather than to boil leafy vegetables. But we should warn readers not to get the steaming kettles usually found in shops, in which the vegetables have to be put in a sieve above boiling water. This extracts the juices. The point is not just to soften vegetables at the risk of leaching out their valuable soluble nutrients. What is really right is the sort of steam kettle that surrounds the contents with a gentle steam pressure.

The best method of all is to let vegetables stew in their own juices with a little fat added.

The above facts are important if we are to do a really good job of preparing nourishing and beneficial food. There are countless different ways for artist-cooks to make appealing dishes by boiling, frying, roasting or serving foods raw, and it should be said that artistic talent is just as important here as technical skill, something that holds true for all works of art. To know one's materials is not enough, especially if all this means is the number of calories, vitamins or trace elements they contain. There must be a deeper respect if one is to come to some understanding of those subtler facts that spur artists to creation. And the housewife, who has this creative sense for what she is using, no longer suffers from the feeling that she is just part of a relentless machine that keeps the household going, but a responsible part of a worldwide organism. This gives her the right spiritual support. Her pleasure in living and doing are enhanced by being made aware that these are cosmic forces she deals with in her kitchen and that, as she effects transformations in the food she cooks, she is really practis-ing the same alchemy in which the cosmos is engaged.

From all that has been said above, it is clear that a raw food diet strains the organism. Of course it is healthy to give it a challenge of this sort on occasion and serve raw carrots or some other root. This is strengthening and stimulating, like building up arm muscles by chopping wood. In general, however, digestion should not be made too difficult.

Health movements of today, supported by science, try to 'get back to nature', and favour 'natural' foods. This usually means a

The influence of the stars on
terrestrial substances

Pictures of the patterns made by apple juice with silver and
gold before and during the solar eclipse of 1.11.1929.

Fig. 13
Control pattern of apple juice with silver.

Fig. 14
Control pattern of apple juice with gold.

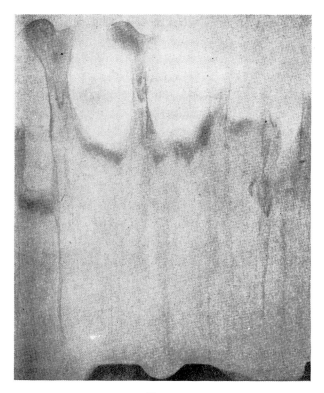

Fig. 15
Pattern of apple juice with silver during the solar eclipse of
1.11.1929.

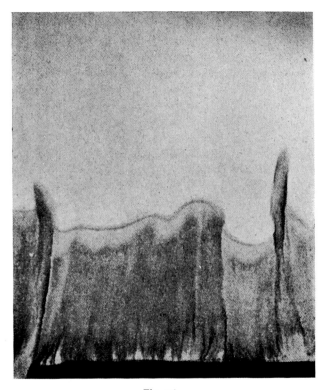

Fig. 16
Pattern of apple juice with gold during the solar eclipse of
1.11.1929

Fig. 17
Juice of raw elder flowers – pattern with gold.

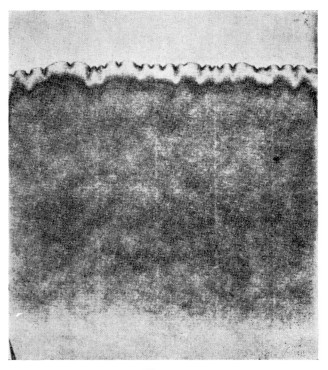

Fig. 18
Juice of elder flowers – cooked for 5 minutes. Pattern with gold.

Fig. 19
Juice of raw celery root. Pattern with silver.

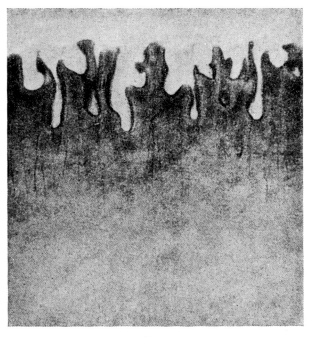

Fig. 20
Juice of celery root – cooked for 5 minutes. Pattern with silver.

Fig. 21
Raw cabbage juice. Pattern with silver.

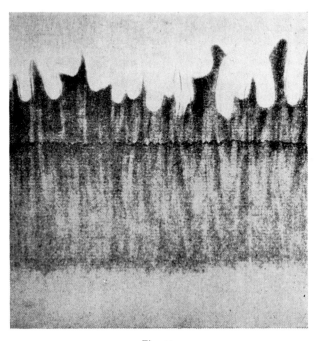

Fig. 22
Cabbage juice – cooked for 5 minutes.
Pattern with silver.

Fig. 23
Cabbage juice – cooked for 20 minutes.
Pattern with silver.

Fig. 24
Juice of raw cauliflower. Pattern with silver.
(Corresponding to the cabbage leaf cooked for
the shorter period.)

Fig. 25
Juice of cauliflower – cooked for 5 minutes.
Pattern with silver.
(Corresponds to the cabbage leaf which
has been cooked to death.)

raw food diet. Their chief concern is a possible loss of vitamins, and with some reason where cooking methods make no sense. Perhaps the above exposition may contribute to forming an idea of how cooking should be done, with the emphasis on transforming rather than destroying food values.

A one-sided raw food diet carried to fanatical extremes all too easily overtaxes the organism, with the result that neither spirit nor body are properly supported, not to mention the metabolic problems that can develop from such a course. Forces that should be serving higher functions are needed for digestion. Shortness of breath, a weakened will and flabby limbs tend to result. On the other hand, thinking is apt to become arbitrary, for the forces that create mobility in this realm go instead to taking care of the raw food.

Nevertheless, a raw food diet prescribed by a physician can work therapeutic wonders. In such cases, rhythm and timing play a vital rôle, and the diet must be worked out in relation to the patient's whole nutritional régime.

Obviously the source of supply must be considered in prescribing raw food diets. Bio-dynamically raised produce is the most desirable. Under no circumstances should fruits and vegetables grown on farms that use sewage sludge or excretory products to fertilize their fields be eaten raw, for this is the cause of the intestinal worm infestation which doctors see increasing at such an alarming rate.

To sum up: Raw foods are therapy, cooked foods nourishment.

CHAPTER TWENTY-TWO

Externals of Cookery

HEAT SOURCES, POTS AND WATER

The source of heat used, the cooking vessel and the water are externals to which people usually pay altogether too little attention. An organism can only prosper in surroundings suitable to it. Food should be an organic work of art, and in this sense the quality of the warmth that penetrates and cooks it, the vessel it is cooked in, and the water into which its essences are drawn, are all decisive factors.

So long as heat remains no more than a question of the number of calories applied to an object in measured quantities to get the technical effect desired, there will be little feeling for fire's inner qualities. And it will seem ridiculous to consider the 100 calories produced by an electric stove to be quite different qualitatively from the same number of calories produced by a wood stove.

But they are different. And there may be a person here and there who has felt how differently a wood fire warmed him on a cold winter afternoon from the way an electric one, operating at the same temperature, would have done. Those who have taken the thesis of this book seriously will fully expect to find that the quality of a given fuel must be reflected in the quality of the fire. Beeches and pines are simply different natures, with nothing in common but the fact that both are trees, and a fire of beech logs therefore has a different quality from a pine-log fire. Bakers confirm this from the experience that has made them sensitive to such things.

Of course a chemist might say, 'Well, beech wood produces different by-products from pine wood: certain tars, guaiacenes and aromatics, and these give bakers the illusion of a different warmth quality.' But these very differences in the chemical composition of a tree are an expression of inner differences of being. And repeated experiments have clearly established the differences in the warmth produced by different fuels.

In these experiments, distilled water was brought to boiling point in a reflux condenser using various kinds of fuel: gas, electricity, coal, wood and straw, and kept on the boil for 20 minutes. The water was then cooled down to 17 degrees Celsius and used as a growing medium for wheat plants. The various test waters heated on the above fuels were then poured out into porcelain saucers and wheat seeds were allowed to germinate in

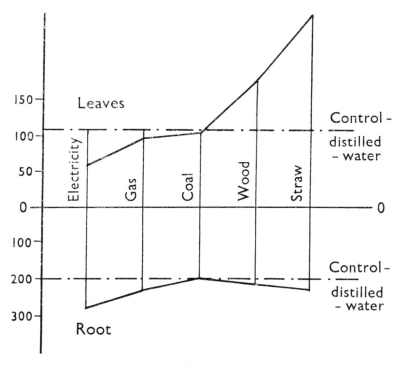

Fig. 26
The quality of heat according to its source (effect on germinating plants).

these media. The interweaving roots gradually formed a mat that held the developing leafy shoots. Again growth was halted on the tenth day to measure root and leaf dimensions, and these were averaged and entered on the chart. Figure 26 shows the average leaf-measurement in the upper curve, the root averages in the lower. We see that the various warmth qualities were transmitted to the seedlings as growth-furthering or growth-retarding forces.

The chart shows that electricity had the least favourable effect, wood and straw the most favourable. To one who has made a study of the nature of electricity this comes as no surprise, for electricity always plays the rôle of a condensing agent. It makes a candle flame turn outside in, making for solidification where formerly there was just the opposite: etherealization. This builds up visibly in a carbon skeleton that forms on the wires connecting the two poles (cf. *The Nature of Substance*). It makes ozone of oxygen by densification. Electric light is thus a materializing force. One might call it a counter-pole to light from cosmic sources, earth's counterlight. Wires set aglow by an electric current are not caught up in the sublimating fire-process that sets matter free to take its way back to the cosmos. Theirs is rather a resistant glow produced by force, the compulsion of the counter-light force. To say this does not signify disapproval or an attempt to turn the wheels of progress backward. We are merely stating the facts.

All these imponderables are more familiar than perhaps we realize. They are reflected in our use of language, as when we say that a woodfire blazes merrily.

Pots and pans are external sheaths for food in a somewhat narrower sense than the more external but completely penetrating element of heat. C. Remer expresses it charmingly when she says, 'Many strange instruments seem essential to the well-equipped kitchen. Let's take a look at pots, for instance. Every cook has something to say on this subject. She always has her favourite pans, and can tell legendary stories about their performance when she feels inclined – stories to which her lay-hearers find it hard to lend credence. They cook so easily and fast and bring out such flavour as to seem like something out of a fairy tale. In any case, pots do play an important rôle. Elements that make for a delicious dish are blended there, and the pot can be proven to affect the blending. Everyone knows that quite different results are obtained from pots according to whether they are made of aluminium, iron, enamel, glass, clay or copper. A pot serves as the skin or sheathing of the food it contains, and food and pot must go well together. It is like a person and his clothing. Not every article of apparel suits everybody; each of us must find the style individually right. This feeling for proper style should hold sway in the kitchen also. And it usually does, for rare is the housewife who picks up the first pot at hand and stuffs her vegetables into it. Rather we see her rejecting pot after pot that stands in her way, until she comes to just the one she wants. This is not mere instinct; it is a matter of expertise gained from experience. Light, cheap, aluminium pots, for example, are known to interfere with aromatic elements in cooking. They stain potatoes and turn barley dark. Milk is apt to get a queer taste and not to keep well afterwards. Aluminium lids are too light and let the steam escape. But iron pots with their great heavy lids are also not suited to delicate vegetables, which are apt to become too sodden in the imprisoned heat. The shatter-proof new glass and porcelain pots and pans are attractive, but I prefer to do my cooking in the old clay casseroles, the broad, shallow ones. And there are certainly foods that require a particular kind of pot. Milk tends to absorb foreign flavours easily, and coffee and tea need special pots for the same reason. And fruit should not reek of onions or some other taste which, while pleasant by itself, does not add anything to compotes. A special pot should be kept for them. Finally, a fine sense needs to be developed for the right weight of lid for this or that particular cooking job, for getting a lid that lets the food breathe properly.'

Certainly the material of which the pot is made is very important. Our experiments were designed to give us reliable information on this score.

To this end, distilled water was boiled for 20 minutes in vessels made of gold, iron, tin, copper, aluminium, glass, porcelain, stone and enamel, and when it had cooled to 17 degrees Celsius, seeds of wheat were set to germinate in it. Their growth was interrupted at the end of the experimental period, and measurements were taken of leaf and root dimensions. This enabled us to ascertain which pots were growth-inducing and which inhibiting.

The curve shows that gold makes by far the best material for cooking pots. This recalls fairy tales which describe eating from golden dishes as the height of good fortune.

Further experiments even showed that stirring with a gilded spoon had something of the same effect. One's pleasure is the more enhanced by observing in the course of these experiments that wooden spoons are second only to gold in good effects, being made of a material grown in sunlight.

No one need be surprised that aluminium showed up most poorly in the tests. It is a metal smelted from clay in electric furnaces, a process that is a drastic forcing. Clay is compelled to take the form of a bogus metal, something quite foreign to its

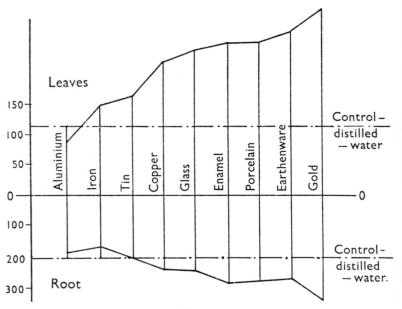

Fig. 27
The quality of cooking pots (effect on germinating plants).

real nature. Functionally, aluminium is not a metal, but an earth. Earthenware pots seem so much more natural than ones made of this artificial metal!

Water provides cooking food with a further, still closer sheath or enclosure. Here it is not so much a question of the mineral components determined by chemical analysis, though of course the calcium in a chalk region is nutritionally important, and so is silica. The radiation that streams out of the earth and into water is far more significant. Famous springs owe their beneficial effects more to the fact that they are fed from the heart-blood of the earth than to chemical properties. The earth is a living organism

The qualities of water
series of crystallizations of saltpetre

Fig. 28
Control crystallization from distilled water.

Fig. 29
Crystallization from water from the spring
of St Odilie.

quite different in the east and west, the north and south, and in its depths. This gives every least spring and brook and river an individual character.

The two crystallization pictures shown above (Fig. 28 and 29) bear out these statements. One is of distilled water, the other of water taken from the Spring of St Odilie in Alsace. They were made as follows: In *The Nature of Substance* I pointed out that crystallizing salts, being themselves immediate expressions of formative forces, make the best medium for testing formative forces in other substances added to them. It has been usual, in mineralogical studies, to concentrate exclusively on shape, angles, edges and surfaces of single crystals. But the spatial arrangement and relationship of the various parts of an emerging crystallization pattern are also significant. These relationships, which give the picture its particular stamp, are very labile and react most sensitively to the slightest formative influence. So, when a saturated solution of potassium nitrate in distilled water is allowed to stand in a crystallization vessel, a pattern such as that in Figure 28 emerges in ten minutes. There is no evidence of a particular directing force to be discerned here, for distilled water is too neutral to contain any such thing. Chemically, the water from St Odilie's Spring is almost identical. It springs from the quartz soil of the Vosges, thus contains no calcium, and has an o-degree of hardness. It is nevertheless famous for its curative powers – the eyes are especially benefited – and has a strong and pleasant flavour. Potassium nitrate dissolved in water from this spring crystallizes in the pattern seen in Figure 29.

We can see here how the earth is permeated by shape-giving, formative forces. Very different qualities show up in water taken from places quite close together.

A supply of good water, strong in formative elements, is an essential in cooking. Generally speaking, any moderately soft and uncontaminated water is considered satisfactory, but these are not sufficient criteria. Well water is often to be preferred to a city supply reeking of chlorine.

Hardness in water is due to the amount of $CaH_2(CO_3)_2$ or calcium bicarbonate it contains. This dissolves in cold water. When heated, however, it breaks up into calcium carbonate, which is not water-soluble, and precipitates, and carbonic acid, which escapes.

$$CaH_2(CO_3)_2 \rightarrow CaCO_3 + H_2O + CO_2$$

The calcium precipitation coats foods as well as pots and pans. This does nothing to help the sublimating process of digestion. There are two ways of avoiding trouble here. One is to pre-boil cooking water. The second is to change the calcium carbonate into a different calcium salt that can be relied on to stay soluble. One way is to use sodium sulphate acid:

$$CaH_2(CO_3)_2 + 2NaHSO_4 = CaSO_4 + Na_2SO_4 + 2CO_2 + 2H_2O$$

The calcium sulphate thus obtained is soluble in the proper concentration and will not precipitate. Sodium sulphate acid can be bought in pill form.

Neither the chemical nor the pre-boiling method is ideal, though the former at least retains the calcium so vital to nutrition. The ideal solution is a natural source of good water, as described above. There is, however, no sure recipe for obtaining it. It is as much a question of destiny whether one lives in a region that provides such water as is the nature of the climate where one lives and works. In unfavourable cases there are always other balancing factors in compensation.

CHAPTER TWENTY-THREE

Preserving

STORING, PICKLING, SALTING AND CANNING

Storing food is necessary in all but the most favourable climates where Nature keeps her table ever richly spread. 'Putting up' for times of scarcity is therefore part of most cooks' jobs, and it may spark their interest in this work to delve into the correct ways of preserving.

In the last chapter we discussed how heating brings about a lifting and freeing, a sprouting, shooting up and ripening of substances. Here we must concern ourselves with the opposite problem: whether a process similar to that of root formation, with its capacity for permanency, can be achieved.

To understand how this can be done, let us once again observe how the threefold plant develops from its centre towards two opposite poles, becoming ever more etherealized as it climbs blossomward, ever more solidified toward the root.

What happens to plants at their earthy root-pole?

Not only do they become materially more condensed: the whole organism takes on a certain permanency. It is at the root that plants develop the lasting qualities that enable them to go on existing. The top of the plant, the parts above the earth, wither and burn up when autumn comes. But roots survive every season.

As warmth encourages blossoming and ripening, cold works down into the root zone, making for permanency of form. How similar to this all preserving is. Freezing, salting, pickling, and all the other methods try to achieve a lasting state, which, like roots themselves, has something of a mineralized condition. All preserving, even when it does not involve refrigerators, tends in this direction.

Again the signal facts can perhaps be illustrated practically by experiments carried out for a whole year, during which period changes that occurred in stored apples were studied by the capillary method previously described. All the apples harvested from a certain tree were laid on piles of straw, and every week one was pressed and its juice examined in a capillary pattern-picture. So long as the procedure was kept constant, the newly harvested apples yielded flame-like forms. But just after Christmas the forms began to split apart and become somewhat crystalline, and by spring definite root forms made their appearance in the midst of the crystalline development. The apples' exterior, too, had changed by this time and become wrinkled and decrepit looking. The rhythmic cycle in the course of which a fruit can be expected to turn into a mere seed-containing sheath – that is, become earth-related in order to strike root and develop new plants – was clearly discernible in the capillary picture as it developed through the seasons. This change began to show as early as Christmas.

The picture we were getting of these processes was rounded off most satisfactorily by the following experiment. In May, when the typical crystalline root forms described above appeared, we tried boiling the sap for five minutes. Blossom forms immediately reappeared in the capillary patterns. They were not quite so beautiful and flaming as those in the autumn pictures, but very similar. This showed that old apples are no longer fully fruits, but have taken on something of the root nature. They are therefore better baked or stewed for invalids, not raw.

The process that gradually occurs in storage is greatly accelerated by low temperatures. All sorts of large and small coolers keep our food from spoiling. But in view of the processes just described it is clear that foods preserved by chilling or freezing need to be 'lightened' again by cooking. Here again, however, it is the how, not the what that matters, and exaggeration is to be avoided rather than this or that particular form of treatment.

There is not a very great difference between chilling and freezing. All the same, frozen foods give one pause. A plant's physical and chemical properties are certainly retained after freezing. But the moment it thaws, very rapid decomposition sets in, and the food looks withered and unappetizing. No one who has eaten frozen fruit, for example, can quite escape a strange reaction. It has to be eaten immediately because it deteriorates so swiftly. And then the fact of having cherries and asparagus in January simply seems odd and unnatural. There is no well-founded reason for forcing things to this extent.

Stored milk undergoes very rapid change, as we mentioned in

a previous chapter. Malyoth found evidence that milk contains sugar in the form of beta-lactose at the moment of being taken from the maternal organism. This substance is an optically active sugar, the expression of the live qualities of the milk. A few hours later, it has changed into an inactive, racemose compound made up of alpha and beta lactose. In our terminology, the milk has taken on root qualities. Cooking cannot restore it to a living condition however. It stays dead and breaks up into the fats, cheese, sugar and salts of which it is composed.

Pickling is a good, cheap way of keeping certain perishable foods over winter. Sauerkraut and pickled beets are favourite winter vegetables, and with some justice. The souring due to lactic acid fermentation is helped along by the salt added to layers of sliced vegetables.

Simple salting also achieves good lasting qualities, as with cucumber and bean pickles.

Drying is somewhat similar in effect. Plums, apples and dehydrated vegetables make good subjects, provided the process is carried out gently and skilfully. There must be no direct exposure to the sun. The danger here, as in all conserving, is of the necessary reduction to a lasting form proceeding too quickly. If it does, the aromatic substances are pressed out instead of being retained.

The least harmful of all preserving practices is bottling in oil, vinegar, syrup and the like, and it is very satisfactory.

Heating, however, is the chief means used. It is entirely different from the practices hitherto described. Instead of turning things in the root direction it brings about an almost total fading.

Foods thus preserved can be considered dust and ashes unless the process provides for the kind of radiating back that occurs when plants form seeds. Roasting and baking do just this. Zwieback is a good example, and dried eggs and powdered milk are produced by the same process.

So-called 'cold canning' occupies a mid-way point between these poles. The heat is kept low (75-80°C.), bringing about a mild 'blooming'. A lid is pressed onto a rubber sealing ring and a vacuum thus created as the jar cools. This not only holds the cover on, but helps the contents of the jar to become more rootlike. *The Nature of Substance* goes into detail on this. A vacuum is brought about by a centripetal sucking action related to the earth's cohesive forces. A study of root functioning shows how typical this pulling, drawing earth-gesture is.

It is not at all a good idea to help these preserving processes along by adding poisonous chemicals. Even such substances as boric acid, benzoic acid, salicylic acid and their salts, alcohol, formaldehyde and hydrogen peroxide are occasionally found in people's kitchens. But they are used on a big scale only by the preserving industry, of which more below.

CHAPTER TWENTY-FOUR

Poisons in Food

CANNED FOODS

More and more homes are making a practice of feeding the family out of cans. There are plenty of reasons for this habit. It is so very convenient. It saves the purchaser having to go here and there to get the ingredients of a meal together and then cleaning, peeling, cooking and seasoning. And then how clean and appetizing it is to serve out of a can! Housewives unfamiliar with the point of view on which we base the nutritional approach set forth in this volume and who therefore cannot enjoy performing the responsible kitchen alchemy which their jobs entail tend to take the short cut. And, of course, with so many women going out to work, what can they do but open cans?

Anyone who picks up a can of food and reads the label is apt to find on it the proud boast, 'Enriched with Vitamin A', or C, or D, and modern thinking tends to convince him that this is a good thing. But there is not much left of the original formative forces by the time the can leaves the factory.

Usually no mention is made on the label of the poisons that have been added to the food to prevent spoilage.* Some countries make it obligatory to list all ingredients. But law-makers have to permit certain amounts of poisons to be used if the food is not to spoil. And since they are also interested in seeing industry flourish, they close an eye more tightly than they should.

The harmful effects of poisons such as salicylic, benzoic and oxy-benzoic acid on the human organism are common knowledge. But it is as well to develop a more comprehensive picture of them here in harmony with the spiritual-scientific approach to man on which this volume is based.

In *The Nature of Substance* I went very fully into the question of high dilutions and the effects they have, and showed that the rhythmical dilution of a given substance releases forces in it that are not available in its denser form. I showed too that a copper

---

* In Germany the producers are nowadays forced by law, to mention on the label the preservatives used.

sulphate solution that has undergone a single dilution is by no means the same product biologically as a rhythmically diluted or potentized product of the same solution. Though the two products may be identical chemically, biologically they are very different. And the more diluted a substance is, the greater is the energy set free. Homœopathy is based on these dynamics.

We will have no trouble understanding what happens with high dilutions if we give up the generally accepted view of substance that conceives matter as imperishable and lend a sympathetic ear to the new conception set forth here and in *The Nature of Substance*. Matter is simply a fixed stage, a 'frozen moment' in a cosmic process. Earthly materiality and cosmic being are two opposite poles with innumerable in-between stages and conditions. And plants are living bridges between these opposites, caught up in countless metamorphoses of shape and substance, subject to rhythms of contraction and expansion, of involution and evolution, alternating pure-being with material appearance. The inspired imitation of these processes in nature: rhythmical dilution, is called 'potentizing'. It could just as properly be called the returning of a manifested substance to its pure-being state.

In *The Nature of Substance* I showed the stimulating or depressing effect which the various potencies had on the growth of test organisms (germinating yeast, in this case). The experiments described gave us potency curves that were absolutely characteristic and specific for a given substance. Studying these curves, one sees that there are substances incapable of the rhythmic response plants demonstrated. Synthetic benzoic acid, a derivative of coal tar, is one such substance, and its curve is so straight as scarcely to deserve the name. Natural benzoic acid, a derivative of benzoin resin, showed quite a different, lively curve with characteristic maxima and minima. Here are two substances, both called benzoic acid and chemically indistinguishable, yet biologically wholly different.

Experiments showed that every substance incapable of being potentized belongs in the same category. To characterize it more dramatically, let us once more resort to the plant for the sake of comparison (Fig. 30).

We will need to look back and consider the development of

the material spectrum of the plant as it proceeds in two directions from a starch basis. In the cosmic process of out-breathing, the starch becomes rarefied into sugar, blossom colours and fragrance, nectar, oil, and healing properties. The opposite, downward development is one of increasing hardness and mineralization

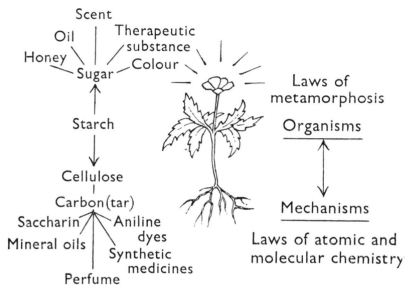

Fig. 30
Organisms and mechanisms (nutrition and poison).

which leads by way of cellulose to the biological zero point, coal tar.

Man's brilliance has conjured forth from coal tar the whole mirror kingdom of synthetic dyes and perfumes, saccharine and other synthetic sweetening agents, mineral oils and synthetic medicines. It is also the source from which preserving, refining and flavouring chemicals are derived, along with the list of synthetic vitamins.

Comparing the two realms in Figure 30, one gets the impression that the upper one, where a balance is constantly being wrought in innumerable metamorphoses between the living poles of sky and earth, is a realm of biological reality and dynamism. The lower, in great contrast, is a subterranean domain that strikes the observer as a ghostly mirroring of the creative cosmic order. There is nothing here of a dynamic quality. Instead, it is a world of atoms ruled by statics. The two realms obey completely different laws. The living plant kingdom and its spectrum of substances is subject to the laws of life formulated by Goethe in the all-embracing concepts of polarity, intensification and metamorphosis. Here potentization is a sort of 'ladder to heaven' up which the plant's various metamorphosed substances climb in lawful, rhythmical progression toward ultimate refinement. The lower realm is governed by the laws of atomic physics and molecular chemistry. Substances here are incapable of responding to rhythm and metamorphosis and they cannot be potentized. One realm is inhabited by organisms, the other by mechanisms. The law of the conservation of matter obtains only in the latter realm.

Coal tar derivatives present in our food may be eaten, but are not digested. They are retained in the organism for some time before being excreted. Some remain for life. Such substances become material ghosts that haunt living processes in a way that is most disturbing, both to these and to soul-spiritual functions.

It is hardly surprising that certain substances used to dress up foods, like the yellow dye used to colour butter, encourage cancer. Kurt Lenzner performed an important service with his book *Gift in der Nahrung* (Poisons in Food), where the various dangers are listed. But it is even more important to be aware of the forces underlying such developments.

Housewives who are aware of this will look at nutrition quite differently and find it brings them quite new responsibilities. One who derives the greater part of his food from the lower, 'mirror' realm becomes impregnated with matter that cuts off his bodily organism from the life of the universe. This makes his body an enemy fortress when he tries to develop and ennoble it in the service of his spirit. Little by little it becomes impossible to effect any changes in it. This is a perspective that must be looked straight in the eye.

More recently a new danger has become acute in the realm of nutrition: pesticides. In order to kill insects and micro-organisms on crops, highly poisonous chemicals are sprayed over the fields and forests – sometimes even with the help of aeroplanes. If that goes on, we shall soon experience the 'Silent spring' (R. Carson). Innumerable deadly illnesses have been caused by this method. Vegetables and fruit have to be thoroughly washed with hot water, especially when they are eaten raw.

CHAPTER TWENTY-FIVE

Modern Dietary Reformers

HINDHEDE, LAHMANN, BIRCHER-BENNER,
MAZDAZNAN, RAGNAR BERG,
GERSON-SAUERBRUCH

In the course of time nutritional science has given rise to a great many mistaken theories which have been widely adopted both by universities and laymen. These theories have done a lot of harm. A few saw where the errors lay and courageously set about exposing them.

The Scandinavian Hindhede was one of the first to speak up against the calory concept. When Voit, in Munich, set one hundred and eighteen grams as the minimum daily protein requirement, Hindhede countered with his conviction, based on experiments on himself, that thirty grams a day were all that were needed. And he went on to attack what he considered too heavy a fat intake. Dark rye-bread, which he thought contained sufficient fat and protein, was in his view the ideal basic food.

Lahmann was one of the first raw food exponents. He also recommended steaming rather than long boiling, and was an enthusiast for cottage cheese as a source of protein. Nutrition was not his only interest, however. He wanted to reform man's whole way of living, and saw the question of dress as most important. The underclothing named after him was very much sought after for a while. Corsets were his favourite target.

One of the great minds in nutritional reform at the beginning of this century was the Swiss physician, Bircher-Benner. He had grasped something of the formative forces at work in nature, for he spoke of 'sunlight as a food', and was concerned with preserving its 'sun energies'. He considered it of the utmost importance to have a 'true reverence for food'. In his view, all preserved foods were 'devalued'. He was of Hindhede's opinion that raw foods and a reduced intake of protein are a *sine qua non*.

Nuts, fruit, root vegetables and whole-grain breads were the basis of his 'whole foods' dietary therapy. 'Bircher Müsli', a preparation made of oat flakes, milk, sugar and fruit, and eaten raw, became quite famous. It would be in keeping with more recent research in dietetics to substitute freshly prepared cereal groats for oat flakes. Cereal grains lose part of their formative forces upon being ground, a fact that poses a bread-making problem which is hard to solve. Of this, more below.

Though the efforts of these men, and of Bircher-Benner in particular, can be acclaimed as a great step forward in nutritional hygiene, it must still be regarded as only one step. That they parted ways with the purely technical view of life and nutrition which prevailed meant a great deal. But man must be looked upon as a being of soul and spirit too, and understood and taken seriously as such, before it is possible to arrive at a full and adequate conception of what constitutes healthy nourishment. One gets the feeling that the reformers mentioned were searching in the dark for the true facts about man, but that they came to a halt on the threshold of the mystery of life. They could distinguish between the alive and the unalive, but soul and spirit appeared to them merely special aspects of the living state. Here we witness the limitations of scientific orthodoxy, which has no organ for Rudolf Steiner's teaching on man's true nature. The fundamental connection of consciousness and soul activity with death-related breakdown functions requires a capacity for seeing how related soul-spiritual and bodily processes are.

We have in the Mazdaznan movement an example of the one-sidedness in dietary matters to which an ancient, solely spiritual tradition leads. It goes back to earliest Persian culture for dietary rules that are no longer really understood. And a failure to grasp the spirit as spirit always means dragging it down to a materialistic level. Nevertheless, the Mazdaznan concept of the proper diet is justified in some respects. 'Master Thought' is the ever-present guiding principle. Discontented, inharmonious natures are not allowed to take part in preparing food. Meals are made ceremonial occasions, with flowers on the table and an atmosphere of spiritual communion. All this is good and proper. But if the reality of the spirit's presence in the physical is not rightly understood, there is always danger of losing sight of large, cosmic aspects and therefore becoming primitive and pedantic. One of the Mazdaznan rules illustrates the one-sidedness referred to:

'Broil what cannot be eaten raw, and eat raw anything that cannot be broiled.'

Fear of an 'impure state' leads to a body cult that easily degenerates into the worst kind of materialism. The frequent washings and irrigations of the outer and the inner man actually reflect a lack of confidence in the power of soul and spirit to work in an enlivening and healing way in body functions. All foods derived from animals are avoided as 'unclean'.

Recognition of the importance of salt in the diet raised further problems. Ragnar Berg advocated an acid-alkaline balance, maintaining that this was essential to healthy physiological functioning. But he also held that there should be a slight preponderence of the alkaline to help regenerate used-up tissue. Here again we see someone getting hold of one corner of the facts with which spiritual science reckons in its view of man, for he had a dim feeling for the various aspects of the human entelechy as they affect physiological functions. Problems of this sort occupied him for decades. He found that even under the most difficult circumstances blood invariably tries to maintain a slight alkaline reaction; it takes terribly severe illness or long starvation to bring about a change to an acid one. He noted that acidification led to tissue disturbances, though the threatened organism at once prompts the kidneys to excrete the acids, which then show up in the urine. Since this takes place before the blood itself turns acid, urine makes a sensitive indicator of how matters stand with the organism's acid-alkaline ratio.

Now it is an interesting fact that vegetables make urine alkaline, while meat makes it acid. What does this signify?

In *The Nature of Substance* alkalis were described as promoters of life, as its sheathing. Even though fruits and certain other parts of plants are acid, alkali is nonetheless the carrier of those formative forces that are responsible for germination and growth. The moment a plant starts to germinate and shoot, magnesium, a base-forming agent, is present. On blossoming, however, acid-forming phosphorus is active in the setting seed. Here, in seed and blossom, soul elements are at work. They only brush the plant, but are fully incarnated in animals. In the foregoing chapter on animal protein as a source of food, we had occasion to speak

168

of the instincts and passions which meat-eating stimulates. Acids are carriers of these elements. We see the same thing happening in food as it passes from the mouth into the stomach and thence into the intestines. The products of human digestion are acid wherever conscious soul activity still accompanies them. Pepsin works in a strong hydrochloric acid medium in the stomach. But at the point where the stream of nutrients disappears into the unconscious depths of the intestines, the realm of living, regenerative metabolic forces, there is an alkaline reaction. Trypsin metabolism is a base-related function.

It need not surprise us, then, if meat causes acidity and vegetables alkalinity. In the light of the above Berg's 'acid-alkaline balance' appears to be the physiological reflection of a harmonious interplay of life and soul forces decisive for health.

The Gerson-Sauerbruch saltless diet is in a class by itself as a recent nutritional departure. These researchers found that sodium chloride excretion is disturbed in chronic illness. All mineral metabolism is unfavourably affected, calcium especially so, as it is excreted instead of salt. Rachitis, for example, was found to build up sodium chloride deposits in the bones while robbing them of calcium. And tuberculosis deposits salt in the lungs, at the same time lessening their calcium content. This led to the Gerson-Sauerbruch diet for the tubercular. Salt is cut out entirely and protein intake considerably reduced, while raw foods are emphasized. The two scientists discovered that protein tends to retain salt in the body. Raw foods, however, supply more of the potassium antagonistic to salt, and so help excrete the latter.

Facts of this kind were learned through the study of pathological conditions. They were then popularized by reform-minded circles and touted as the only proper diet for the healthy as well as the ill. However, orthodox science too came to recommend a lower protein intake and pointed out the value of raw foods, thus lending a good deal of support to the reformers.

Just as our carbohydrate metabolism reflects the way the soul interacts with physiological processes, so mineral metabolism supplies the foundation for ego activity, for the intermeshing of the spirit with the body. If the ego acts too strongly and thus tears down the body, as in consumptives, this deposits too much salt in the lung tissue – a fact that certainly calls for dietary therapy. But therapeutic diets should not be considered right for everybody, sick or well. Unsalted food eventually takes the ground out from under the spirit in each one of us, cutting us off from a future in which we have the task of enhancing our capacity to digest minerals in order that the spirit be increasingly present in bodily processes.

Here we have an example of the slow, painstaking and detailed work and observation that has to be done to build an exact scientific foundation for understanding facts which Rudolf Steiner presented decades ago in his picturing of man. Those scientists who have worked at this deserve our gratitude, for they have provided the data that cannot be found by spiritual research. But it takes both kinds of research to work out the real picture of man-the-spirit in physical embodiment on earth.

CHAPTER TWENTY-SIX

Suitable Modern Methods of Preserving

ADJUSTMENT TO COSMIC RHYTHM

Preserving was described earlier as an attempt to bring about in food the permanency that is the natural condition of plant roots. And we saw that going too far and passing this point leads to biological zero, the borderline at which a caricature-realm of matter begins developing out of coal-tar, a realm of wholly dead substances. Indeed, they are so dead that they cannot respond to rhythmic stimuli such as potentization, nor be woven into the life of organisms. From this dead realm we derive preservatives.

Orthodox science subscribes to the view that micro-organisms, fungi and decay bacteria, are responsible for the decomposition that takes place in organic substances. Obviously, the logical treatment then is to kill such micro-organisms. This is accomplished very thoroughly and methodically either by sterilization or the use of poisons.

Approaching the problem with the eye that 'sees what is meant in the thing seen', one discovers that micro-organisms are not to be looked upon as the *cause* of the spoilage, but rather as the by-products of retreating life. Every phase of life in the cosmos has its rhythms. Universal life becomes caught up in organic complexes and then deserts them again. In other words: the physical manifestation created by a being falls apart and 'dies'. There is no such thing as eternal life for any living organism here on earth. Instead, it has its own special rhythm, which inevitably brings death. A cabbage taken from the place where it grew and put into storage does not last long, and the rate of decay in more fragile vegetables and juicy fruits is even faster. What we see happening here is a retreat of life from its physical-organic base. The particular complex of forces that provides life with a carrier is just as real and coherent an organism as the physical one which every living thing possesses. When the latter dies, the life organism undergoes dissolution. Micro-organisms feed on this retreating life. They are symptoms of decay, not its cause.

We see another case of the same kind in contagious disease.

Bacteria should not be regarded as the *cause* of illness; their presence indicates that the life organism was already unbalanced and therefore 'disposed' to become the feeding ground of specific micro-organisms. Orthodoxy does not, of course, see things in this light and is still addicted to the germ theory of bacterial infection. But there is a new movement in medicine that recognizes the facts, though space does not permit our describing it further here or going into the question of how it regards the passing of germs from one person to another.

In killing micro-organisms, then, modern preserving methods merely suppress symptoms of decay. But this also means suppressing the very thing they were intended to preserve: the living organic complex. Put in orthodox scientific terms, vitamins are destroyed. All that is left is a purely physical substance in a mummified condition.

What can be done to consolidate life in an organic nexus and keep it from escaping? What means are there of lengthening the life-span of fruits and vegetables? Technologists of the future will no longer ask how they can most reliably do away with micro-organisms, but rather how they can anchor life so firmly in a plant that micro-organisms find nothing there to feed on.

Actually all we have to do is to go out into nature with our eyes wide open and note how flowers open in the morning and close at night; how plants germinate and shoot up in springtime, reach a peak of development in summer, fade away in autumn, and last through the winter as seeds able to germinate and shoot up anew. Those who can feel something of the power behind these rhythms will recognize that all of nature is carried by rhythms. Rhythm, in short, is the life element.

On walks in the German countryside one can still come across baroque castles here and there where an old gardener tends his plants and flowers devotedly, and sometimes with an old-time wisdom. Such an old fellow may show a passer-by his 'flower-clock'. This has a cosmic mechanism. It is a circular bed divided into twelve sections, in each of which grow flowers that open at a certain time of day. The first section may open its blossoms at six in the morning, the second at seven, the third at eight, and so on, until six p.m. Observers' hearts are moved by the unity witnessed in the connection between heaven and the responding earth.

Space has been given both in *The Nature of Substance* and in these pages to a description of research carried on for decades to determine the rhythms in which plants take up and then release again material substances. Definite evidence was gathered that life's rhythmic laws obtain here and are the guiding principles of material creation.

In view of the facts brought out by these experiments, we may confidently predict that the problem of preserving foods will find its solution in a linking up of each living complex of substances with cosmic rhythms.

Such ideas have already borne fruit in their application to Bio-dynamic agricultural practices. We showed above that a truly modern agricultural chemistry must take the rhythms of universal processes into account. Rhythms of the juxtaposition of sun, moon and earth, as well as planetary rhythms, play a most important rôle in farming, though as yet we are far from understanding them fully. The farmers who practise these new agricultural methods as well as those fortunate enough to have access to their products will all testify to the fact that vegetables, fruits and grains grown Bio-dynamically have sufficient concentrated vital forces to stay fresh through the winter and even longer, while the same categories of foods grown by other methods have long since deteriorated.

It may be possible in later publications to indicate how these same new methods of preserving can be applied with equal success to other realms as well.

CHAPTER TWENTY-SEVEN

Bread

Our daily bread is the most basic of our foods. But how many transformations it has gone through before reaching the form we are familiar with today! They make an interesting study, for they are a prime example of the fact that changes in human consciousness bring about corresponding dietary change.

Let us look into the original form which bread took at the time when Zarathustra was teaching his disciples to raise cereal grains. People of that period simply crushed the berries and added milk or water to make a paste. It was characteristic of the time that most foods were eaten in this semi-liquid form. The reason was that people's consciousness was 'spread out' through their cosmic and terrestrial surroundings. They were not yet capable of thinking thoughts with contours to them. Thus they felt no need to have their metabolisms come to grips with solid food. Modern dietitians are familiar with the fact that puréed foods make those who eat them phlegmatic and not too prone to energetic and original thinking. On the other hand, porridge is entirely suitable for children not old enough to go to school and to have to think logically.

The next step in the evolution of bread came in early Greek times. The Greeks are described as making bread before the days of Troy. Flat stones were heated and a porridge-like mixture of grain poured over them. This baked into a sort of flatbread, or cracker. We may ask ourselves what this hardening process signified. And we can see that it gave people a chance to come to grips, in the very food they ate, with earth's physical hardness and solidity, at the moment in time when they were beginning to do their own independent thinking and were on the verge of developing Greek philosophy.

The next metamorphosis of bread occurred in Hebraic culture, with the Jews' discovery of sour dough or leaven. From this time on, bread had an inside and an outside, with its crumbly interior encased in hard crust. The inside is always full of small air holes, which are made by the introduction of air in the leavening process. Bakers and housewives know what a different thing dough becomes when it is worked, or kneaded: it is given a chance to breathe. And when it is allowed to stand and rise, when the dynamic effects of the kneading start to make themselves apparent, the dough swells, and we see something going on that can only be likened to drawing breath and becoming a living organism.

Not only is the leavening very interesting in itself – it is also characteristic of something basic in Jewish feeling. Old leaven which has been kept over from past bakings is put into the new dough. Then part of the new batch is saved and used to leaven the following one. Thus, significantly, the leaven keeps going a connection between successive bread bakings. Something of the past works over into the present, the present into the future. It is like rhythmical breathing, with an erstwhile out-breathing leading to a new in-breathing, the in-breathing to another out-breathing, and so on. Following the whole chain back to the first loaf is very much like tracing generations in a family line. Something of the original substance has been handed down through every baking right up to the present, as Father Abraham's blood flowed down through and linked all his descendants. How like the family consciousness of the Jewish people from the earliest times! It dates back to the period when individuals thought, felt and acted purely out of tribal instinct. They experienced their common blood so strongly that some even remembered the deeds of long dead ancestors, as it were inheriting their consciousness in the hereditary stream. A man was reckoned as old as the number of years his memory reached back, which explains the great age of Methuselah and the other patriarchs.

This sort of consciousness, somewhat diluted and with the variations which national characteristics impart, was the one prevailing in Europe in the Middle Ages. A capacity makes its appearance first as an isolated evolutionary step, only to become the general possession of humanity in a later epoch. Family, clan and national feeling ran high indeed throughout the Middle Ages among European peoples, overwhelming the individual.

In the fifteenth and sixteenth centuries a still further change occurred in bread-making. Shortly before the French Revolution a decree went out in Paris stating the rules on baking the new yeast-bread, which bakers of that city had to follow. The use of yeast marked an extremely important moment in bread's history. Ancestral ties were abruptly terminated and each loaf put on its own, as it were. It is easy to see the change in consciousness that went hand in hand with this development. The fifteenth century was the period that marked the beginning of a new sense of selfhood which set a man apart from the rest of the world. Attendant on this was a new reaching out to bridge the gulf with man's various organs of perception, which led to the development of natural science and started a wave of exploration whereby, with the discoveries of such men as Columbus, Vasco da Gama, etc. the whole earth became man's familiar possession. Clan and family ties started to lose their stranglehold as individuals felt increasingly independent.

This marks the beginning of personal development.

Chemists soon found that machines and chemicals could take the place of the kneading and rising that had hitherto kept bread-making so alive and natural. Many commercial bakers nowadays impregnate their dough with carbonic acid in air-tight mixers and use baking powder instead of yeast.

When such means are resorted to, the end-product comes dangerously close to being just a burnt-out mineral. The intimate process wherein air was supplied by the housewife's kneading and to which she could feel personally and enthusiastically related through the creative spiritual labour of her hands can scarcely be duplicated in big, city bread factories.

But these technological developments run parallel to modern man's type of consciousness. He has developed his personality, to be sure, and has a sense of personal freedom, but in relation to the material plane only. And the freedom he feels is expressed for one thing in the fact that he can choose among all the forms of bread reminiscent of its various past phases, from porridge and 'müsli' to crisp-bread and crackers, home-made bread, and finally the factory loaf. The means are present to stimulate all the different levels of complex modern consciousness, and a man has only to choose freely from among them.

As we have repeatedly pointed out, the way is being prepared for a spiritual fulfilment the dawn of which can be glimpsed in the character of Goethe. The development of thinking and its penetration into the creative realm of universal thought reflected in Goethe's living concepts will become the goal of the immediate future. Rudolf Steiner showed the way in his *Philosophy of Spiritual Activity* and other works. But this new development of consciousness also requires bread to take a corresponding new form. In the years ahead, the human consciousness that was narrowed down to a small self-awareness must be widened again. But the cry must not be 'Back to nature!' with its return to the good old days and ways where food is concerned. New ways will have to be pioneered. There must be further steps in mineralization, but they must be characterized by increasing fineness, transparency and mobility, moving in the direction of 'the wisdom of salt', not that of the cinders of dead fires.

Cereals, as we know, are all wind-pollinated plants. This means that they are lacking in a true blossom process. Is it not a good idea to supply it in the form of honey, which, as an ethe-realization of the salt process, is a link with heavenly wisdom?

Honey and salt stand at opposite poles of rarefication and density, creating between them a dynamic field. Rudolf Steiner indicated that the new form bread would take would be the product of this honey-salt interaction.

Experiments along these lines led to the very interesting results shown below, and these held up so well in practice that the new bread referred to is already in production here and there.

Neither sour dough nor yeast, and certainly not baking powder, are used in this bread. Salt and honey take their place, and the bread rises under the influence of the tension between them, aided and abetted by proper kneading methods. It is significant that the rising occurs at sunrise. Systematic experimentation allowed time-variations in the intensity of the rising process to be determined.

The curves registered by the bread's steady rise showed a strong upward surge around six a.m. Yeast bread rose just as steadily at midnight. Both kinds of dough were mixed, kneaded, and set to rise in the early evening hours.

The question of what flour to use solved itself when it appeared that the process worked only with freshly ground grain. Other researchers too have found that milled grain soon loses much of its value. Whole grain can be stored almost indefinitely, but flour spoils quickly. In the above experiments, however, it was discovered that the grain not only had to be freshly ground, but the curves also showed how important the husk elements or rind-forces were to a successful outcome. Much has been said in earlier

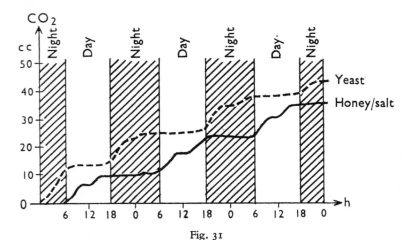

Fig. 31

The working of yeast and honey/salt as a diurnal process (the yeast 'goes' at midnight, the honey/salt at dawn).

chapters about the significance of the forces inherent in grain husks and in the salt which the rind-forming process develops.

A further very favourable circumstance was the decision to use a mixture of four kinds of grain, which now comprise the ingredients of the new 'four-grain bread'. A harmonious balancing of these four grain-temperaments not only has a stimulating effect on the whole organism: the improved action of the honey-salt process demonstrates how well the fourfold 'build' of this flour is adapted to the alchemy of bread-making.

The most interesting fact of all is that only Bio-dynamically-grown grains work in this new process. It is clear that grain in which cosmic rhythms have been strongly developed will reflect the rhythm of the sun tides in the field of tension generated between salt and honey.

Formative forces in bread

Series of crystallizations with saltpetre (see control
crystallization Fig. 28).

Fig. 32
Picture of the crystallization of a crumb.

Fig. 33
Picture of the crystallization of the crust.

The honey was a special problem, for it was not always possible to find a quality suited to the process. When it proved difficult to get the bread to rise we usually found that the honey came from bees fed over the winter on beet-sugar syrup.

It was further observed that the bread's quality was affected by the fuel used. All bread used to be baked in the home. Nowadays, however, with time always at a premium, we have come to use all sorts of newfangled mechanical ovens that bake at higher temperatures and do the job faster. Steam ovens were tried instead of wood-fired ones, and technological progress eventually came up with electric ovens. Quality declined with each new invention.

It was not long before we settled on wood ovens for our honey-salt bread experiments, and we kept the temperature considerably lower than is usual. Though this lengthened the baking time a little, the bread so baked was properly 'ripened', and had a really marvellous crust.

The important thing in this baking process is to keep the bread thoroughly alive, retaining the living formative forces of the grain. The crust must not be baked to death and immobile, but should positively radiate shape-giving and transforming forces.

We have frequently pointed out above how well suited the crystallization method is to demonstrate subtle forces inherent in a given substance (cf. *The Nature of Substance*). Saltpetre (potassium nitrate), for example, clearly showed its formative forces in the single crystal. But the total picture made up of these crystals as they crystallize out of the solution in a shallow plate follows no particular law of form (cf. Fig. 28). But when a drop of plant extract is added to the salt solution, the plant's formative forces imprint themselves on the crystal pattern. This explains why the ice-crystal patterns on a florist's window are entirely different from those on the butcher's. Similarly, drops of extracts made from breadcrust and the inside of the bread and then added to crystallizing solutions of potassium nitrate result in graphic demonstrations of the difference in the formative forces inherent in these two parts of the loaf (cf. Figs. 32 and 33).

Bread is thus the prototype of both the earth and each least seed. And just as we found the ordering forces of the cosmos present in bran, the husk element, so a well-baked breadcrust may be looked upon as a source of supply of these nutritionally important ordering forces, which also work in the sense of the 'wisdom of salt' to stimulate conscious thought processes. The inside of the bread, however, nourishes the ensouled body.

So truly is bread man's archetypal nutriment that one cannot look at it from any angle without coming upon some new revelation of man's nature. We saw this in the evolution of bread through history.

★ ★ ★

We described the lily and the rose as the two representative plants. Cereals and fruit (bread and wine) have always been considered basic foods. They play an important part in relation to the life of Jesus. He was born in Bethlehem, the 'City of Bread', as the name signifies. And when Christ refers to himself as the 'bread of life' he uses bread as an apt symbol for the perfect communion between heaven and earth in a sanctified human body. He whose vehicle it was, says Herbert Hahn, quite literally broke bread with his disciples at the Last Supper. And in his first words he expressed the holy mystery of bread.

CHAPTER TWENTY-EIGHT

The Philosopher's Stone

Today there is much basic misunderstanding of the search for 'the philosopher's stone' pursued by the medieval alchemists. In the early part of that period there was an esoteric school, to which some men subjected themselves, which sought the transmutation of substances, and finding the philosopher's stone was an attainment on that path. Alchemists looked on the various substances as expressions of cosmic shaping forces. They spoke of the 'signature' of a substance, meaning the way it came into being and disappeared again, and how it was related to universal processes. Ancient scientists and doctors (and this would include Paracelsus) still knew something of the esoteric traditions of antiquity. And the secret of the philosopher's stone had to do with the 'signature' of carbon.

We can try to form a picture of the nature of carbon with the help of modern scientific insight if we look at it in its universal aspect. This will help us grasp what the philosopher's stone is in a way relevant to a new age. And it is one of the purposes of this book to further just such insight.

Carbon occupies a very important position among earthly substances. It is the basic stuff with which nature builds the organic kingdoms. It forms the scaffolding not only of our foods but of the carbohydrates, fats and proteins that make up our bodies. When these substances break down upon being heated in a test tube, they leave a carbon residue or 'skeleton' which usually keeps the shape of the original substance. A piece of charcoal still clearly shows the structure of the wood as it was before burning. Carbon is thus a skeleton or armature used by life as a basis for its building and shaping.

Chemists are familiar with carbon as a shaping agent, for this aspect has given rise to what is called structural chemistry. Substances are pictured as having charged 'arms' or valences reflecting the number of other atoms with which they can combine. Oxygen (O), for example, has the value two, and it combines with two hydrogen atoms of the value one to form the compound called water. Thus the formula for water is H-O-H. Carbon has the value of four, and is thus capable of combining with four single-valued atoms. But it has still further capacities not possessed by other substances: it can combine with itself and so form an infinite number of compounds, expressed in branching chains, rings and so-called condensed structure which are the basis of organic (carbon) chemistry. More than two million such compounds have been recognized and described. Comparing these with the 70,000-odd compounds made by the ninety-one other elements gives us some idea of what a remarkable substance carbon is.

Structural formulae of organic compounds expressed in terms of carbon are quite properly and picturesquely called 'carbon skeletons' (cf. *The Nature of Substance*). No matter what one may think of the atomic theory on which they are based, these formulae do, in fact, reflect reality: the reality of the tremendous shaping power of carbon.

As a food, carbon is an exceedingly important substance, for it is lifted by the metabolism onto higher levels in man-the-microcosm, to work at the shaping of bodily substances. But this is not the whole story; it also plays a decisive part in the life of consciousness. Some day we will learn to regard earthly substances as processes come to rest, as the ancients did when they used the term 'the end of the paths of God'. Then we will see the specific qualities of a substance (its 'signature') as a free force, not necessarily attached to matter, whose place of origin is some distant spot in the universe. The starry world radiates energies and qualities which fall on earth and are there condensed into substances. The same energies and qualities also function here, on the level of living processes, as etheric formative forces. The carbon process is the shape-giving element, both in the bodily and spiritual spheres. Carbon is responsible for our ability to form mental pictures of the universe that we call concepts. It enables us to think in unison with the shaping thoughts of the creative cosmos. We owe the structural element in our thinking to carbon energies at work in us. In *The Nature of Substance* I showed that these shaping energies responsible for form wherever it is found in man and universe originate in the constellation Scorpio. In earlier times Scorpio was called The Eagle. St John, the writer of the loftiest of the four Gospels, was Eagle-inspired. He composed glorious pictures not only of our remotest past but of the future. Tradition links him with the Eagle signature.

Man is the meeting place of carbon's terrestrial shaping forces (which he takes up in his food) with the shaping forces of the Eagle taken up as cosmic nutriment and in his 'structuring' consciousness.

Carbon forms plants by working in the assimilation process that produces a visible substance, starch. It condenses starch into cellulose, the structural material of the vegetable kingdom. This hardening process reaches its peak in roots, whose decay leaves carbon corpses or skeletons, which form peat, then lignite, and finally coal, which is taken into the bosom of the earth.

Iron, which is everywhere in the earth's body, comes together with carbon at this point. There are no two substances with a stronger mutual attraction. Pure iron is soft; it can be forged, rolled, drawn, and stamped. But when it is red-hot, it has such an affinity for carbon as to dissolve and absorb it, and thus become hard. It acts on carbon as water does on salt. This is the origin of steel and cast iron. Thus carbon may be said to harden and fix iron in its shape. But some of it is separated out again as graphite on the surfaces of the cooling casts. *The Nature of Substance* describes these processes at length.

Iron then, is not the only substance to be changed by its encounter with carbon: the carbon also changes and becomes graphite. But the goddess nature brings about an even more miraculous happening. When iron has been heated red-hot to melt it for casting and is very quickly cooled, carbon also separates out, but this time not in the form of graphite, but of diamonds. When a piece of the casting is broken off after cooling, it is found to have little diamonds scattered through it. The carbon itself has taken on shape, translucency and hardness; it has undergone a purification that has lifted its substance to the loftiest state matter can attain: that of a 'precious' stone. Alchemists were thoroughly familiar with this ennobling process whereby amorphous matter was raised seven stages to achieve transparency and become a gemstone. It seems as though when black, opaque carbon turns transparent it is recalling its cosmic light-origin in suns of long-forgotten summers. It has carried the sun's formative energy down through every stage of shaping being, from that of pure spirit to the ensouled, the living, and finally the physical. As a diamond, in its brilliance it seems a substance made of light, the epitome of harmonious form.

This is so remarkable a process that one gazes on it in the deepest reverence. It can be a symbol of our own cosmic task where the body is concerned. For our bodies too are built of carbon. It is carbon that shapes the proteins of our organs, nerves and muscles and blood components. Here, too, carbon encounters iron in its organic compounds. It is iron in our warm blood that is the ego bearer in us and puts our bodily substance through a heating, firing and transforming process.

Man too has a long development behind him. He too once had a body made of light, which, in man's fall, suffered corruption and became the shrunken, darkened thing we know today. It was possible for only a god to bring redemption by entering such a darkened body and completely transforming it into a 'risen' one. This mystery having once been enacted, every human ego is now free to become one with the powers of resurrection thus engendered. He who rose from death is the representative of man who points out his earthly task and shows him how to accomplish it. And when it is accomplished, man will again have a body made of light, a physical body comparable to the diamond, but with life's flexibility, a substance that has been purified to the highest level of which live physical matter is capable.

This transformation signifies the stage the alchemists called 'the philosopher's stone'.

In the first communion, Christ broke bread with his disciples, thus identifying himself with the earth that it symbolized. He became one with the body of the earth when his blood flowed on the Mount of Golgatha. Since then the earth is our Lord's body.

Those who think of asking in what parts of the earth diamonds occur will find a most interesting and significant answer in a map of the localities (Fig. 34).

The best-known diamond mines are at Diamandino in Brazil and Sumatra, together with the Malayan Archipelago. These localities are Equatorial antipodes. A line drawn between them would have to pass through the centre of the earth, and is thus one of its diameters. A further well-known place is the Transvaal, in South Africa, and a somewhat less well-known one is located in the Sandwich Islands of the Pacific. These latter also lie on an earth-diameter that cuts the first one at right angles. This makes

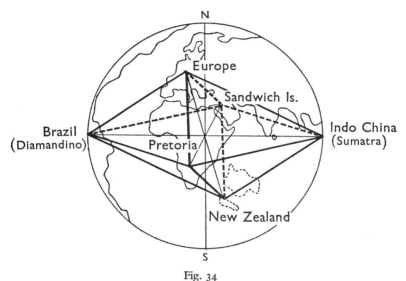

Fig. 34
The Philosopher's Stone
The world's diamond mines (joined) produce an octahedron.

the two lines into a cross, and their intersection coincides with the earth's centre.

Now New Zealand is also a place where diamonds occur. If we draw a line from there through the centre of the earth, it comes out in Middle Europe, where, though there are no diamond mines, the diamond-related Eagle forces have been at work in the spiritual life of Central Europe through the last 3,000 years of its history, making it a nurturing ground for great thinkers and helping to prepare mankind to grasp the most significant of its events: the mystery of Golgatha. This diameter in turn cuts both the others mentioned at right angles. If the terminals of these axes are connected by straight lines, we get an octahedron, the pattern of all diamond crystals. Earth's body is thus structured like a diamond, the perfect earthly symbol of creative sunlike shaping forces (Fig. 34).

The entire organic world on which our senses open is given shape by carbon. It is a world full of the working of wise law. Infinite wisdom has surrounded us since time immemorial. But one element is missing in it, the very element that we feel to be the core of our mission here on earth. That element is love. Nature is amoral. She has not yet needed to concern herself with good and evil. Man, in his freedom, is the only being charged with guarding and fostering this knowledge that he bought so dearly with his Fall. It lies in the power of his soul alone to change knowledge and wisdom into love, love that flows into creative and redemptive deeds through man's union with Christ's resurrective power.

It is man's mission here on earth to make a cosmos of love out of a universe of wisdom. This means, in the language of the alchemists, to make the philosopher's stone a stone of love.

ADDENDUM

Practical Dietary Indications for the Sick and Well

by

GRETHE HAUSCHKA, M.D.

GENERAL REMARKS

Those charged with the care of both the sick and the well can be guided to rational practice by a timely new approach to nutrition that views every problem in the light of a really large perspective.

This book has harped on the fact that there is no such thing as a ready-made ideal diet. Instead, each individual should be given the sort of food that stimulates his particular body, soul and spirit and keeps all their various processes and functions very much alive.

Feeding even the healthiest people is a responsible job impossible without true insight into human nature. Young people growing up need to have some attention given to developing their metabolic forces to the fullest, avoiding the paralysing effect on the higher man of a monotonous and insipid diet on the one hand, while seeing to it that the metabolism is not thrown out of balance by being called upon to do too much. A sensible management of youthful diets can prevent much later illness, while indifference lays the basis for it. It is most important here to make wise and patient efforts to overcome the food dislikes so often found in children, lest they become fixed in harmful one-sidedness. Tiny tastes of the food they think they cannot bear help the organism to adjust to and gradually get to like it. Tact, fantasy and fondness do wonders for the child, for every single food that a person becomes able to digest and like makes its special contribution to that individual's very real and important capacity to deal with and gain mastery over matter. This is far kinder than weakly giving in to children's whims. There is room for just as much courageous and adventurous action on the child's part here as his heroes ever demonstrated in meeting their challenges.

The perspectives developed in this volume point to the need for co-ordinating spiritual growth with that of the bodily organs which can only serve it properly with the help of a right diet. The same perspectives point the way to a sane handling of diets for the sick.

Diet belongs to a realm somewhere between medication on the one hand and nutrition on the other. It can be treated in such a way as to make it almost wholly either. The man of science tends to want to prescribe foods as he would a remedy. But it is important for the patient himself to take part in establishing the diet that is right for him as an individual; it must lie somewhere between prescription and free choice, for a person's attitude in this plays a far greater rôle than is usually recognized. Sometimes a food which is all wrong from the dietary angle, but which the patient enjoys, agrees with him better than the supposedly right thing that he would have had to force down. The point is to be reasonable and not carry things too far. And there should always be a fresh, creative aspect to every diet. Even with diabetics it is not good to stick too rigidly to weights and measures, but rather deal livingly with living facts of nature.

To do this, one must have an accurate picture of the forces inherent in foods such as that which has been developed in preceding chapters. Then substances taken from the various natural kingdoms can be properly adjusted to man the microcosm. Diets can then supply the forces missing in his sick organism and avoid foods that might have a poisoning effect.

But here too it is more important to build up a capacity to digest foods which the organism could not formerly tolerate than to keep to some prescribed diet that could permanently discourage the metabolism from developing new powers. Patients ought to summon up the courage to branch out occasionally and add something to the menu. We should realize what an anti-social thing it is to stick to a diet and be unable to tolerate this or that food, once the acute stage of an illness is over and such caution is no longer warranted.

In the following pages we will therefore sum up briefly nutritional principles as they apply to healthy people, and then proceed to show how they should be adapted to the sick. It will not be necessary to go into great detail on diets, but merely to indicate the guiding principle that applies in a given instance. We cannot attempt to deal here with every conceivable food, but those who intend to make a practical application of the principles to be discussed will find sufficient orientation in the general aspects.

The magazine *Natura* has devoted an issue (Vol. VI, no. 3) to articles by Drs G. Suchantke, Ilse Knauer and the author outlining such dietary and nutritional principles and their application at the Klinisch-Therapeutisches Institut in Arlesheim near Basel, Switzerland.

NUTRITION IN CHILDHOOD AND YOUTH

Considerable space was given in preceding chapters to a description of the way each individual life, in accordance with basic bio-genetic laws, repeats developments in the evolution of the race as a whole. This fact alone can give us a basis for determining the order in which healthy children should derive their nutriment from the various natural kingdoms. First comes mother's milk (up to about the sixth month of infancy), then cow's milk, then vegetables (beginning with the fruit or seed element in cereals and working downward via the green leaves and stems to the root element), and, finally, salt.

This descending scale is attuned to the descent of an individual into earthly incarnation.

An embryo uses the plastic forces of the mother's blood to build up its organs. When the child is born it continues to receive plastic forces in the milk secreted by life processes in the mother's organism. These plastic forces are taken up in easily assimilable form in the proteins, carbohydrates, fats and salts that serve as their physical carriers. Mother's milk makes for the wonderful atmosphere of growth governed by cosmic rather than earthly laws in the child's still sleeping organism which has not as yet undergone differentiation and become bi-polar. It is a period during which the organs (those of the brain and nerves first, followed by the lungs and heart as organs of the rhythmic system, and finally by the metabolic organs) must have time to grow without being hardened prematurely by terrestrial forces.

The whole inner complex of organs is conditioned by milk, the 'divine' food and drink of ancient times, to change over without too much difficulty to the earthly functioning involved in digesting foods from nature's other kingdoms. Even cow's milk, coming as it does from the animal kingdom, presents a challenge that not every child takes in its stride. For this reason it is good to dilute it. Children are exposed at weaning to influences from their earthly surroundings. They shed protective shells, as it were. We often see how much more vulnerable a child is that has not had the blessing of its mother's milk for quite long enough.

At the fifth or sixth month a transition to products of the plant kingdom can be thought of. Fruit and seed elements are the best to begin with. Infants can be given teaspoons of freshly pressed fruit juice. This tends to stimulate quite different forces, those of feeling, of inner perceptiveness. Fruit acids such as those of oranges, tangerines and raspberries stimulate the soul to enter a little more deeply into the body. Stronger tastes like those of spinach and other leafy vegetables, not to mention roots, are related to salts present in them, and have the effect of stimulating sense activity and strongly grounding the new earth-citizen.

All this while milk is being used with cereals, first farina and oatmeal, then with sago and rice, in an increasingly thick consistency, until a transition to bread can be attempted.

Young children are still so wholly enwrapped in warmth processes that they need almost no fats. The best thing to give them in this category is tiny specks of butter on their porridge.

Milk intake should be gradually reduced. Ordinarily a child should not have more than a quart a day after his first birthday.

Evidence of a normal descent and activity of a childs' higher principles, as these affect his life-body's development, is to be found in plastic changes in the skull, the gradual closing of the fontanelle, an increasing definition of form in his features, weight increase, a rosy skin, and general indications of a lively coursing of the body fluids. Mobility is the criterion by which one can tell how the soul forces are intermeshing with the body. Babies who tend to zestful kicking and flexing, who like to look around them, who have healthy breathing, digestion and elimination rhythms are certainly taking hold of their vital functions with the soul and spirit. Voluntary motions begin to be purposeful at the fourth or fifth month. The eyes, too, really focus on objects, and the baby reaches out and takes hold of them, certain of his aim. This shows that the ego of the child has entered the picture and is experiencing itself as a separate entity confronting an external world. One could go on and on listing items of evidence that indicate the awakening and activity of man's higher principles as these show up in an infant's development. It is a mighty drama, signifying a conquest of the world, here represented by the body, and it consists of many other most essential phases such as timely teething (there are twelve by the time the child is one year old), sitting unsupported, standing erect, walking and learning to talk.

Those familiar with the spectrum of 'awakeners' among foods will be able to find the right means for supporting the child's incarnation process. First there should be a gradual reduction in the amount of milk given. Then come fruit juices, puréed leafy vegetables, and finally root vegetables (the first of which should be carrots because they conduct the blossom process all the way down into the root). By these means one can stimulate every function, from the metabolism upward to the breathing process, and lastly, the activity of the senses.

To reduce the diet of infants to a rigid schedule results in later impoverishment of the powers of imagination and affection which are all connected with a child's nutrition. A set programme exerts every bit as deadening and paralysing an influence as do the 'sterile' nurseries in homes concerned only with guarding children against bacteria. How much more alive the situation is where the mother follows her baby's development with love and imagination and has some feeling, as she prepares a gruel, for the connection of the various cereal grains with the elements: knows the relation of oats to warmth, of barley to light, of rye to the heaviness of water, and wheat to all four – expressed even in the patterns of their way of growing. Such a parent sees to it that the child is given raw instead of refined sugar, in order that the purely mental powers thus stimulated are not called upon prematurely and the baby's organism hardened before the right moment of development. And she will avoid experimenting with its subtle cosmic-earthly balance by giving it all sorts of titbits from the grown-up's table.

Great caution should be observed in the matter of meat and meat broths, for these weight the child down to earth too strongly, besides introducing into his unfinished organism foreign elements that interfere with and disturb the ego in its work on the organs. It should not be forgotten that in their first years of life children are making their bodies into the instrument on which their healthy soul and spiritual functioning will have to depend later. Meat is not the only thing to avoid in early childhood. Wine and beer are especially harmful, and strong seasonings, mushrooms and eggs should not be given. These foods tend to sever the child's connection with cosmic forces in which it should be immersed at this period, and to subject it too early to differentiation and hardening processes. The internal organs are not yet properly integrated with the higher forces that should govern them, with the result that these forces are 'on the loose' and disturb the organism. A diet of the above foods, sometimes given to 'strengthen' its recipient, only produces nervous, restless human beings who tend to asthma and all sorts of allergies. These indicate that the soul and ego, instead of helping create life in the organs, only succeed in producing irritants.

All this shows what a responsibility the proper care of healthy children is. But the needs of sick children and those with digestive troubles can also be understood far better in the light of the body-soul interrelationship described above. In a stubborn case of constipation, for example, medication is not the only resort: fruit acids, blossom products such as sugar and honey, or malt, can all be used to stimulate the inner motility proper to the metabolism. These substances possess activating powers. They ease the tendency to intestinal blocking and have a synthesizing, moderating effect on the action of the liver. The metabolic processes become more fluid under their influence. Where an opposite, loose condition prevails, liver action can be stimulated by the formative element inherent in protein. Protein-fortified milk can be given, for example, or strained rice-gruel, which has a highly plastic action and passes only very slowly through the intestines.

Nora von Baditz has written a most instructive booklet on the education of young children (*Was braucht das kleine Kind?*) in which she distinguishes three phases within

THE FIRST SEVEN-YEAR PERIOD

– phases which I now propose to discuss from a more specifically medical standpoint.

Children lay a bodily basis for the life of consciousness in three stages.

The first such period begins at birth and lasts through the first two and one-half years of life. The brain and nervous system are the organs chiefly developed at this time. A child spends more time asleep than awake during this period. The rule here should be, 'Do nothing that could disturb the peace and interfere with the subtle work of perfecting going on here, for the nervous system is the bodily reflection of the macrocosm and takes star patterns as its model.'

Nature's wisdom should be given free rein. Earthly food and the cosmic nutriment received through the child's sense should be kept very simple and natural. Then the child can work out and develop the best nervous system that his own needs and nature permit. Civilization, with its omnipresent radio and other equally crass disturbers of the peace, its interference with body and senses in the matter of toys and gymnastic contraptions for tiny babies, its cramming in of protective foods and vitamins, commits sins the disastrous effects of which can hardly be calculated.

In the second period, which lasts till approximately five, the middle system is consolidated; breathing and blood circulation become adjusted and harmonized. Every kind of rhythmic experience furthers bodily development at this period. It can be movement, as in games and play. It can be the stimulus that plenty of variety and tasteful colour arrangements in the foods on a child's plate mean: the easily digested vegetable and fruit dishes; crispness; the contrast between liberating sweets and concentrating salt, and warming spices (especially those of the labiate family). All this makes for a well-regulated metabolism. A good motto for this period would be

Maintain lively interchange between child and
world through enlivening rhythms.

Just as it takes a properly developed nervous system for the child to become a thinker when the time is ripe, so a properly developed rhythmic system makes for courageous, adaptable. sympathetic soul capacities.

The third period rounds things off by developing the metabolic and limb system and thus leads up to the change of teeth. Earth forces take a stronger hold on the child's legs and arms. Play should occasionally give way to easy jobs. The menu can now include more mineral elements. Peas and beans can be introduced, along with a variety of starches and egg dishes. These foods lend weight and substance to the metabolism, and are therefore good for children at the age when they need to become a little more anchored and 'sobered down'. After the second teething the plastic life-forces that previously served to build up the physical organism are freed from that task and put instead at the disposal of consciousness. Children now develop the capacity to remember, and are therefore ready to begin their schooling. We must emphasize again and again how harmful it is to call on thought and memory before the change of teeth. To do so means using up energies needed to round out the development of the internal organs, and may result in all sorts of later disturbances. It can even lay the foundation of such serious illness as schizophrenia. This third period is one in which a child works at establishing the bodily basis for his will life. A suitable motto might be:

> Anchor the will in the metabolism and exercise it, both by giving the child earthier foods in moderation and by engaging him in regular tasks and responsibilities. He should also have some form of artistic movement such as that offered by eurythmy.

It makes it much easier to deal with illness and deviation from normal patterns of development if one has first acquired a picture of what is normal and how the right diet aids and supports it.

A child may, for example, have a tendency to hasten the closing of the fontanelle and to rush into a premature differentiation and consolidation of his organs. He may also be the scattered, restless, too-wide-awake type, with a very small head in proportion to the rest of the body. In such a case one does well to emphasize the sweet and aromatic blossom element in the child's diet. He should be given milk for a longer period to keep cosmic forces working plastically on his organism, and have plenty of green leafy vegetables to help his rhythmic system get well rounded. Children of this type often have a weak metabolism. They tend to be thin and easily irritated. Everything mechanical fascinates them. The intellectual powers wake much too early and tend to undermine the organism before it has been fully developed and established. It is very important to see that such children work a lot with colour and form and are constantly encouraged to live in the imaginative element. This calls into the picture what has been described as the cosmic nutritional stream and helps the senses do their part in the total effort to anchor and consolidate too flighty a metabolism.

Just the opposite course must be pursued with little dreamers who lag behind in their development, finding it hard to loosen their ties with their pre-earthly paradise. Their rather large heads show that the living water-processes, out of which form should gradually coagulate, continue on beyond their time. Root decoctions should be given with their meals to stimulate such children's head forces and so foster proper bone development. Later capacity for thought and judgment depends on a stabilized body with a well-contoured brain and organs. There is a tendency, in children with large heads, for the metabolism to work up into the sense functions and make them blurry and unfocused. Children of this type are prone to headache and catarrhs. They are also more sensitive than others, and are deeply upset by the shocks to which modern civilization subjects them, or by choleric be-haviour witnessed in their homes or surroundings. They must have very gentle, patient handling as well as a diet geared to their needs if they are to lay proper hold on their bodies.

This shows how insight into the normal development of the threefold organism, which must function as a harmonious whole to be really healthy, helps us to understand deviations that can cause illness and, if a kind destiny allows it, to restore balance.

Now let us take a look at

THE SECOND SEVEN-YEAR PERIOD

This period has much in common with the second phase of the first seven-year period in that its chief emphasis is on the development of the rhythmic system. Building the physical body was the main focus of the first seven years. The second seven go to working out the special character of the individual's vital functions (the life-body), which we then witness in his particular temperament. There are four distinct temperamental types, named in accordance with Hippocrates' concept of the four body-fluids, and each is the result of a preponderance of one of the four elemental formative forces in the total chemistry of man's fluids-system.

In the chapter on seasoning agents, reference was made to the fact that temperament is an expression of the vital (or life-body) level of one of the four parts of the human entelechy. Paracelsus lists them thus:

> Yellow gall
> Blood
> Mucus
> Black gall

The ego's fire works in yellow gall, the soul nature in our coursing blood, vegetative life in mucus, and the mineral-related forces of the merely physical make-up in black gall. There is great wisdom in these rather child-like and unfamiliar terms that have come down to us from the Middle Ages, and a study of them at once gives us a clue as to the parts of the body to which man's four principles relate. We will find that temperaments are based on the mysterious chemistry of vital juices.

Temperamental imbalance should be overcome as a child grows up. A suitable diet greatly helps educational efforts to achieve such a harmonizing.

Fiery-natured cholerics should be given leaf and stem vegetables, along with watery ones like squash and cucumbers. Such foods are light and do not heat the blood. Oats in their various forms should be given very sparingly; they can be replaced by rye. Fruit, which affects circulation so favourably, is a must. Such children should be served raw vegetables frequently. Those like celeriac, radishes and horseradish radiate downwards through the metabolism and prevent congestion. Choleric children are more deeply imbedded in their physical bodies than those of other temperaments, so that it is advisable not to tie them down further with a lot of meat or legumes. Instead, the five forces active here should be directed upward by a largely vegetarian diet. Then these forces are caught up and refined in the breathing and circulatory systems, rather than allowed to become congested in the metabolism.

Sanguine children, with their light and airy, flighty natures and metabolisms, need to be helped to get their roots down to earthy things. They must be fed foods that give the metabolism much to do. Wheat and rye make excellent cereals for them, along with farina, macaroni, noodles and spaghetti, Indian corn, nuts and almonds. Then too, well-seasoned, spicy dishes help rouse and waken their internal organs and tend to make the ego participate more actively in the bodily processes. Meat is good occasionally because of the earthy firmness it encourages.

Phlegmatics need to be waked up with the help of every kind of warming spice, sharp-tasting roots, mushrooms, fruits, and fruit salads. One should hold back on milk, substituting instead teas made of various flowers and served with lemon or some other sharply acid fruit-juice.

Melancholic children also need the blossom element and warming foods to relieve them of the oppressive heavy spirits they derive from too strong a connection with the earth and the gravitational forces that belong to it. Sweets too are very good for them. They should have cream, caramel and honey. Sweetness as a quality is truly 'heavenly', while 'bitterness' is a quality of earth. Tropical fruits, blossom teas, cakes and cookies, with hors d'oeuvres of raw vegetables, all help the little melancholic.

Again and again we see that this or that quantity of fats, carbohydrates and proteins is not the criterion to go by, but rather the quality, the formative forces that live in substances as a result of the processes that brought them into being. Housewives could take so much more pleasure in their otherwise burdensome kitchen duties if they would concern themselves in this way with the nature of the substances they are handling. A child's diet, in this second seven-year period, ought to be conceived with as much imagination as his education, for this helps his rhythmic system, the basis of feeling, to develop freely during a period of the utmost importance to his whole later life. The quality of his breathing and blood circulation actually does make a difference in his attitudes and helps determine whether he becomes a timid or a courageous person.

Somewhere around fourteen, there begins

THE THIRD SEVEN-YEAR PERIOD

in which the ego becomes anchored in the metabolism. Puberty and the change of voice are signs of its complete descent. While the metabolism needs to be warmed through thoroughly at this period, it should not be crammed and stuffed with food. Now is the time, however, for the young forces to test themselves on a grown-up diet. It is the age at which the ego works out the bodily basis for will activity, which is tied in physically with the proper functioning of the liver-gall complex. Occasional exposure to sharp and bitter flavours, such as those of dandelion, wormwood, sage, horseradish, or grapefruit, ginger and the like, stimulates the liver and helps the will to develop a right connection with the surrounding world. It is obvious that alcohol taken at this time has most damaging consequences.

Everyone knows that children in their teens simply cannot be filled up. This fact is a clear indication that the ego is hard at work in the metabolism, digesting food to produce that individual warmth needed both to hold its own against the coldness inherent in intellectual functioning and to support all the heightened limb and will activity in which the young world-conqueror feels the urge to engage. Excellent quality is the only alternative to overwhelming quantities of food at this period. Healthy sources of fats and protein are to be found chiefly in nuts, dried fruits, cheese and cottage cheese, sweet and sour cream, and a coarse and filling dark bread, plus the sweet puddings that are such favourites with teenagers. Meat is a question of individual taste, but should always be taken in very moderate amounts.

Dietary Suggestions for the Sick

Fever is actually a curative factor in disease. Nothing could be more mistaken than the way we try nowadays to bring fevers down as quickly as possible. A temperature is the ego's instrument for taking strong hold of the organism and fighting the invading illness. It should be interfered with only when it goes on too long and begins to weaken the patient unduly.

The fever diet is a simple one, easy to grasp. It should be fluid, cooling and salt-free. Fruit juices and blossom teas are used to aid elimination, for the fire processes active in a heightened metabolic rate break down harmful elements, and these must be removed. The patient really wants nothing else, so that it is seldom necessary to prescribe a diet. If some special preference is expressed, it is wise to give in to it and try it out, for the ego is more than usually active in a feverish person, with the result that he has a good instinct for his needs which the doctor does well to heed. If the fever lasts, the patient will need building up, of course. He must then be given carbohydrates, milk, and milk products. But in order not to weaken the ego's fight against the invader, this should not be done at the onset of a feverish illness. Measles and scarlet fever can perhaps be taken as examples of feverish illnesses of childhood and used to illustrate the proper dietetic approach to cases of this kind.

The upwelling forces of the life or vital body preponderate in measles. Exudative processes are rampant in all the body's mucous membranes, especially in the upper parts, causing conjunctivitis, a running nose, and bronchial inflammation. Sheath-forming, shape-creating forces, such as those supplied by lemons, fruit-skin teas, finely grated raw greens and steamed root vegetables, must be included in the diet. Milk and carbohydrates are to be given only in great moderation, while the silica forces present in stems and fruits should be employed to strengthen the forces of the head region and so avoid that much-dreaded complication: infection of the middle-ear.

Scarlet fever is connected with the break-down forces of the soul body. These work their way into the physical organism and decompose proteins. The resulting danger of nephritis shows how deeply this destructive inflammation penetrates the metabolism. A milk diet is particularly suitable, together with cottage cheese and nourishing fruit compotes made of dried plums, apricots and peaches. Later on, light farinaceous foods are good. Little salt or protein should be allowed, but sugar and starches help rebuild tissue. There should be a generous intake of fluids throughout the course of the disease.

RHEUMATISM DIET

Much emphasis has been laid in these pages on the fundamental fact that our conscious functions owe their existence to breakdown and excretory processes, which have to achieve a balance of sorts with the upbuilding process of protein formation. Uric acid excretion plays a most important rôle here. We need to produce uric acid and to impregnate the brain and nervous system very subtly with it in order to develop the degree of consciousness suited to wide-awake ego functioning.

The metabolic organs, on the other hand, have to be protected from impregnation of this sort by lively excretory activity. If more uric acid is produced than the ego can cope with, or if this happens in parts of the body that have no way of excreting it, it is discharged into the tissues, where it constitutes an alien element. The problem here is to strengthen the participation of the ego in the warmth processes and to avoid serving foods (animal protein, in this instance) that tend to introduce alien activities into the organism. Particular care should be taken to avoid this in cases where the patient has inherited a weak ego–organization. Weakness of this kind is the reason why, in the final stages of the illness, the body becomes deformed; its shape is always the work of the ego.

The rational procedure here is to keep to a purely vegetarian diet, using no animal protein except milk and milk products. The warmth and excretory processes should be activated as much as possible. Sugar should be given in the form of honey and caramel.

Three stages of the disease are usually recognized:

(*a*) the acute, inflammatory stage
in which the principles governing fever diets should obtain: fruit, fruit-juices, and blossom teas to enliven circulation and excretion, a greatly reduced fat and protein intake, milk preferably sour milk, buttermilk, yogurt or kefir;

(*b*) the sclerotic, hardening form:
the most important thing to do at this stage, which tends to gouty and other deposits, is to stimulate the warmth processes by means of hot blossom teas (elder and linden), seed decoctions, whole-grain soups, oats in various forms, and such warming, seasoning elements as fennel, anis and caraway, with fruits and teas to further elimination;

(*c*) the deformative form:
At the stage where the bone and cartilage process is affected, formative forces must be called into play. Steamed roots, such as celeriac, parsnips, carrots, the roots of parsley etc., must be given, together with plenty of sweet things to strengthen the ego organization, and a great variety of vegetables. Ordinary table salt should be used very sparingly in all such cases, since those afflicted with rheumatism are unable to cope with mineral substances satisfactorily. This means that salt taken in any quantity simply forms new foci of inflammation. Raw food diets should be prescribed for a given period during the acute inflammatory stage only. In the other stages it has proved best simply to include something raw in the menu occasionally. However, only leafy, blossom and fruit elements should be used, never roots, as these require too much effort on the part of the organism, withdrawing an inordinate amount of warmth from it during digestion. And it must be obvious that alcohol has an absolutely devastating effect on those who incline to rheumatic disorders, due to the fact that it sets up what might be called a counter-ego in the blood.

TUBERCULOSIS DIETS

In tuberculosis we find both chronic hardening and dissolution processes. The latter come from a preponderance of metabolic forces that surge up into the lungs. The calcifications indicate that ossifying processes are at work as well, trying to turn the lungs into a head of sorts; for the head, which in man is the root principle, is the point of origin of ossification processes. Here we see what happens when the middle part of man, the breathing function, is encroached upon. The upper and lower poles of the organism meet in a way that was not intended as the metabolism surges upward from below and the encapsulating process proper to the head intrudes from above.

Thus we have to distinguish between the exudative and the shrivelling, hardening forms of this disease.

We have already made mention of the fact that the leafy element acts particularly on the middle man: lungs and circulation. In

The Exudative Form

these leafy vegetables should be served in raw juice form or in salads, while such sheath-forming fruits as lemons, oranges, nuts and apples are to be preferred. The formative root and stem vegetables are better served steamed than raw in this case.

Where the illness takes

The Shrivelling Form

leafy vegetables are in order. Among fruits the tropical kinds and berries, grapes, melons and cucumbers are the most suitable.

It is especially desirable to make use of the vital forces present in milk warm from the cow and eggs still warm from the nest.

In general, the diet should be kept low in salt and should consist mainly of vegetables. Honey and raw sugar help support the ego's up-building activity. Since the lungs are organs that play an important part in forming human protein, plenty of nourishing food should be provided, but this should not be exaggerated until it seems like fattening an animal for slaughter.

CANCER DIET

Cancer is a disease that tends to take more individual forms than other illnesses. This is due partly to the fact that it can appear in any part of the organism, from the bones to the skin. Spiritual science sees the cause as an attempt to 'build a sense organ in the wrong place'. It is therefore an intrusion into the domain of the metabolism on the part of the nerve-sense process. The illness is preceded by a long series of psychic as well as bodily involutional phenomena. Those prone to it suffer from depression and with-drawal; they turn their attention inward, as it were. The final stage is one in which the forces of the ego-organization, whose function it is to shape the human form, disengage themselves from one or another stricken organ, something that normally occurs only in the case of sense organs. The result is that the physical principle gets out of balance and forms a tumour.

This is, of course, an extraordinarily complex happening, which space will not permit our characterizing in any but this very sketchy form. We attempt it here only in order to create a basis for understanding the dietary suggestions to be made below.

Disturbances of the warmth system always precede the form-ing of an actual tumour. The lungs fail to clear themselves fully of carbonic acid, which then accumulates in the blood. The lymph stream tends to form blockages and flow less freely. The chemistry of the cells changes. Finally there is a total collapse of the in-dividual's shaping powers.

Since we have to deal here with a kind of suffocation of the tissues and with blood-lymph blockages, we must do everything we can think of to rouse and stimulate the patient's breathing. A vegetable diet activates tissue breathing and elimination far more effectively than does animal protein. In an article in the magazine *Natura*, Dr Suchantke calls attention to the fact that scientists think cancer patients ought not to be flooded with the growth hormones found in plants, and for this reason prefer to prescribe plenty of meat, cheese, and other proteins of animal origin. This opinion rests on a mistaken picture of the dynamics inherent in vegetarian foods. The bodily functions stay far more elastic when body and soul are not tied together by large amounts of protein in such suffocating proximity. Diets consisting largely of proteins bind the spirit to the bodily functions. Cancer-ridden people have a hard enough time dying without adding this further deterrent; they have become so deeply involuted that to find the way out again is very difficult.

Sleeping at night also constitutes a problem for them. This is further reason for emphasizing vegetables, fruit, and blossom elements, with their freeing action. Grapes and tropical fruits are a great help in combating the ever-present threat of self-intoxication. Teas made of caraway and fennel seeds or of elderberry blossoms and other flowers, with honey added, help to keep the metabolism going and counteract a chronic tendency to bloating. Quince and grapefruit juice prove valuable in fighting queasiness. Milk is more easily digested in the form of yogurt, buttermilk, or sour milk. Raw foods should be given only on the side or for very short periods, as stimulants or elimination aids, as otherwise too much of the patient's strength goes to digesting them. Cereals should undergo a roasting in order to stimulate the metabolism and generally support processes of the warmth organism.

We must limit ourselves here to a bare statement of principles. In actual practice, individual needs have to be taken into consideration more fully than in any other illness. But we must call attention to the necessity of avoiding tomatoes and early potatoes in cancerous illnesses, for experiments made by Dr Ehrenfried Pfeiffer prove beyond question that these plants actually do teem with forces of proliferation. Restrictions should be placed on the intake of legumes and the coarser, bloating members of the cabbage family.

If Bio-dynamic vegetables can be supplied, the whole configuration of the vital body will be very favourably affected, for in cancer this body loses touch with cosmic formative forces. We have to note the tragic fact that there is very much in our present civilization that breeds cancer, and among causative factors must be listed those influences that tend to discourage spiritual and bodily participation in the cosmic process and reduce the breathing interchange between man and world. This eventually leads to involution.

Radio, cinema and the social egotism of modern life on the one hand combine with overdone sports, physical hardening from too much exposure to the sun, artificially fertilized crops, canned foods, and too much chemo-therapy on the other to create a milieu in which cancer can only keep on increasing as the typical illness of the age. This makes it more than ever important to provide those threatened by a cancerous condition with every conceivable stimulation of the cosmic nutritional stream, which enters through the senses, to engage them in art-therapy which can unite them again with upbuilding cosmic forces. Painting, music and eurythmy should be pursued to the full extent of the patient's inclination and capacity, and will prove powerfully healing factors. The writer has had two decades' experience of the benefits of properly conducted art-therapy, and can testify to its tremendous value in the treatment of cancer patients. It is not difficult to see how the involutional process can be gradually reversed as the sick person comes to grips with colour in the act of painting.

The legitimate sense functions should be stimulated and made more active in their own proper sphere. This works deep into the organism, makes the glands function better, favours healthy breathing in the tissues, and shows most convincingly that man can be healthy only if he achieves balanced, rhythmical interchange between himself, as a being of soul and spirit, and the world around him. And there is such a thing as proper diet where cosmic nutrition too is concerned, and that is art-therapy as pursued within the framework of spiritual science. The patient's function here is active and creative, an intensive involvement in doing that counteracts his illness. Tackling a task, he is freed from the distressing passivity of merely 'being treated' that would otherwise be his whole lot as a patient.

Indeed, in all internal illness art-therapy is the proper diet from the standpoint of cosmic nutrition. We mention it here especially because it provides such essential help in treating cancer.

ECZEMA DIET

The catastrophic malnutrition that has been the lot of Central Europe is largely responsible for the tremendous recent increase in eczema and proneness to it. There are two distinct types: the dry, miserably itching, scaly type, which makes the skin coarse and sclerotic, and the runny, occasionally even suppurating dermatitis.

In the case of

Dry eczema

we often find that subtle metabolic functions of the liver are impaired. In all such cases protein intake should be restricted and the patient put on a potassium-rich vegetable diet, low in salt, and only very mildly seasoned. Raw foods can be included in it. Sharp cheese, smoked fish and meats, and other such spicy delicacies instantly bring about a worsening of the condition.

Everything must be done too to stimulate the warmth organism of the liver so that the patient's body-chemistry becomes more active and works to cleanse the metabolism fully of the irritants that would otherwise find an outlet in the skin.

Treatment can be supported further by giving the patient wormwood and yarrow tea, dandelion or sage leaves, grape sugar and honey. Alcohol is of course definitely inappropriate, but a grape cure can be very helpful.

The opposite kind of eczema is

The moist, often suppurative type

which appears in the form of eruptions and is often accompanied by a failure of the kidneys to perform their eliminative function properly. Both factors can be involved, and it is not unusual for more than one organ to become deficient.

In eczemas of this kind, a raw food diet or even a period of fasting helps. Substances containing silica, together with blossom and stem elements, should be made use of, with a view to activating kidney function. Teas made from equisetum, birch leaves, barberries and solidago are all useful aids. Protein intake should be reduced, and fresh butter is the only fat that should be included in the diet. Milk is best taken in the form of buttermilk, sour milk or yogurt. Cottage cheese is permissible. Onions are to be avoided as much as possible, while the peripheral formative forces of the skin are helped to function more adequately by sloe juice, juniper berries, blackberries, or bilberries, which contain tannin, a root-related substance.

SCLEROSIS AND GERIATRIC DIET

As a person ages, the up-building forces of the metabolism suffer natural decline. The ego organization gradually withdraws from the warmth processes of the body, becoming ever freer to work in the soul and spiritual principles as the physical basis of life is increasingly mineralized. If this mineralization process and the decentralizing of the ego are under control, things go well, and aging means a progressive freeing of the spirit. When sclerosis is present, however, we find the blood system becoming involved in the mineralization process. Salts, over which the ego then has no control, are excreted in the wrong places. The person's whole outlook is narrowed and bound to the body, making the person childish. This is the picture in an advanced case of sclerosis.

We can see here more clearly than in any other illness what a distinction has to be made between the individual spirit that works through the body's warmth processes and the merely soul or animalic principle, referred to in these pages from time to time as the soul body. This latter principle is to blame for discharging salts in the wrong places in sclerotics. Processes related to coldness now take over, and the metabolism can no longer digest minerals.

Here again, the right diet helps. All releasing and warming influences, such as are to be found in the blossom and fruit elements of plants, can be called upon. Hot drinks are most important, and should be given frequently. Furthermore, an easily digested vegetable diet that steers clear of all forms of cabbage and legumes is indicated. Steamed onions and a touch of garlic here and there are good if the patient has no trouble with them. Meat and salt should be reduced drastically.

While it is a good idea for sclerotics to eat less, all their food should be highly digestible, which means preparing it carefully with this in mind by proper methods of boiling, steaming, roasting or frying. No raw foods should be given here.

In the chapter on milk and honey, we discussed the rôle that honey should play in the lives of aging people. Even when an older person is not afflicted with sclerosis he should be helped along the road to excarnation in the same way that a child is helped to incarnate. There is no point in burdening elderly bodies with substances that stand in the way of a proper loosening of bonds between the soul and the body. Simplicity and refinement should be the keynote in food for the aged. Nowadays we actually go counter to what is ideal because people have no understanding whatever of man's return to the spirit from which he originally came. Instead, there is a great struggle to stay young to the last minute. This means foregoing wisdom. The serenity that might bless a life that has been fully lived is not realized, with the result that fear hangs over people to the last. It makes them cling feverishly to matter instead of using it freely and then abandoning it gratefully when their term on earth is fully spent. An old person's body might be called the ashes left by the fire of his spirit. But if life was lived foolishly, the body cannot get rid of the residues left in it, and these become a burden that will not let the spirit free itself.

Thoughts of this kind no doubt sound strange to modern ears, especially when they are embodied in a book on nutrition. But we can find our way forward to new ways of life only by relating the basic truths that are our human concern to the higher reality of the spirit. Spiritual science has a therapeutic function to perform in this, for it follows the spirit into matter itself. This puts it in a position to effect a gradual healing of the rift between spiritual need and materialistic science that runs through our entire culture.

Bibliography

Aristotle: *Categories – Letters to Alexander on the World System.*

Berg Ragnar: *Die Vitamine*, Leipzig 1922.,

Dieffenbach, Albert: 'Die Bedeutung der Gewürze', *Natura* III 365.

Goethe: Naturwissenschaftliche Schriften. *Kürschners Nationalliteratur*, Bd. 114-116.

Hartmann, O. Julius: *Der Mensch als Selbstgestalter seines Schicksals*, 6th edn., Frankfurt 1950.

  – *Menschenkunde*, Frankfurt 1941.

Hauschka, Rudolf: *The Nature of Substance*, Rudolf Steiner Press, 1983.

Herzeele, A. Frh. v.: *Die Entstehung der unorganischen Stoffe*, Berlin 1876.

  – *Die vegetabilische Entstehung des Phosphors und des Schwefels*, Berlin 1880.

  – *Die vegetabilische Entstehung des Kalks und der Magnesia*, Berlin 1881.

  – *Weitere Beweise für die vegetabilische Entstehung der Magnesia und des Kalis*, Berlin 1883. (Wiederveröffentlicht in R. Hauschka, *Substanzlehre*.)

Hessenbruch, H.: *Moderner Goetheanismus, ein Weg zu neuer Kultur.*

Kipp, Friedrich: *Höherentwicklung und Menschwerdung.*

Knauer, Ilse: 'Die Ernährung des Kindes', *Natura* VI 99.

Kolisko, L.: *Sternenwirken in Erdenstoffen.*

Kollath, Werner: *Lehrbuch der Hygiene*, Stuttgart 1949.

Morgenstern, Chr.: *Wir fanden einen Pfad.*

Natura: Zeitschrift zur Erweiterung der Heilkunst, Years I-VIII, Rheinverlag, Rheinfelden.

Pfeiffer, Ehrenfried: *Kristalle*, Stuttgart 1930.

  – *Die Fruchtbarkeit der Erde.*

Poppelbaum, H.: *Mensch und Tier*, Basel 1928.

Suchantke, Gerhard: 'Ein geheimer Bauplan in den Naturreichen und seine Offenbarung in den Salzen', *Natura* IV 89.

Steiner, Rudolf: *Knowledge of the Higher Worlds and its Attainment*, The Rudolf Steiner Press, 1976.

  – *Philosophy of Freedom*, The Rudolf Steiner Press, 1979.

  – *Christianity as Mystical Fact*, The Rudolf Steiner Press, 1972.

  – *Goethe's Conception of the World*, The Rudolf Steiner Press.

  – *Vom Menschenrätsel.*

  – *Makrokosmos und Mikrokosmos.*

  – *Arbeitervorträge 1923.*

Steiner-Wegman: *Fundamentals of Therapy*, Rudolf Steiner Press, 1983.

Recommended Further Reading

Kolisko, E. and L. *Agriculture of Tomorrow*, Second Edition, 1978, pub. Kolisko Archive Publications, England

Fyfe, Agnes. *Moon and Plant Growth*, Capillary Dynamic Studies, pub. Society for Cancer Research, Arlesheim, Switzerland

Kolisko, E. *Nutrition No. 1*   (3 lectures)
            Nutrition No. 2   (2 lectures)
               pub. Kolisko Archive Publications, England

Kolisko, E. *Nutrition and Agriculture*, pub. Kolisko Archive Publications, England

Kolisko, E. *Twelve Groups of Animals*, pub. Kolisko Archive Publications, England

INDEX

Rudolf Hauschka

THE NATURE OF SUBSTANCE

Translated from the German by Marjorie Spock
and Mary T. Richards

This book is the result of many years of research by the author, which has
given a new perspective on the nature of matter and hence suggests a new
orientation of the sciences. This revitalisation of the sciences, it is argued, can
be brought about by the non-materialistic observation of matter, through a
change in the way we observe phenomena, actively 'thinking into' things –
not merely a recording of measure, weight and number and the accumulation
of scientific explanations that result in a rigid world of hypotheses and theory.
The work is a companion volume to Dr Hauschka's book on nutrition.

ISBN 85440 424 4   Second Edition, 1983   256 pages   paperback

RUDOLF STEINER PRESS, LONDON

George Adams and Olive Whicher

THE PLANT BETWEEN SUN AND EARTH

and the Science of Physical and Ethereal Spaces

The philosopher Schelling once said, 'To know Nature is, in effect, to recreate
the world in man's own mind. This is true Science.' It is the merit of this book
to have applied geometrical imagination and mathematical reasoning in
recognizing the formative forces which can be seen at work in living nature,
thus discovering or re-creating a further realm in the threshold of a new
world, and bringing about a true synthesis of art and science.

ISBN 85440 360 4   Second Revised and Enlarged Edition, 1980
paperback   208 pages   102 black/white ill. 20 col. plates

RUDOLF STEINER PRESS, LONDON

Theodor Schwenk

SENSITIVE CHAOS

The Creation of Flowing Form in Water and Air

Foreword by Jacques Cousteau

The two life-giving elements of Water and Air are throughout the world
threatened by pollution. Water, the source of all life is a living element whose
essential nature has never yet been adequately recognised. This book which
contains over eighty full page photographs and numerous sketches has been
rightly hailed as the first authentic treatise on the phenomena of Water and
Air.

ISBN 85440 304 3   Third Impression, 1976   144 pages text
88 black/white plates   paperback

RUDOLF STEINER PRESS, LONDON